To Mikayla

SACRED OBLIGATION

Yours on your way!

THE STORY OF
"AMERICA'S COP"

Best Wishes
Tony Losito

ANTHONY M. LOSITO

Printed in the United States of America

US Copyright Number: 112780092791
Library of Congress Control Number: 2023913184
ISBN: 978-1-7361932-8-0 Paperback
ISBN: 978-1-7361932-9-7 E Book
ISBN: 978-1-7361932-7-3 Hardback

Author: Anthony M. Losito
Author Consultant: Company 614 Enterprises, LLC.

Cover Design: Anthony M. Losito, Nabin Karna
Collaborative Design and Composition: Anthony M.J. Losito, Amy B. Losito

Content Contributions: Aidan M.M. Losito

This novel is based on the true events of the life and career experiences of Anthony "Tony" M. Losito. These are his records and memories of the events. Memories are not infallible. Please keep that in mind when enjoying the story. The names of some characters, locations, situations, and circumstances have been changed.

All views and opinions expressed in this book are those of the author and do not represent the views of the United States government, the State of New York, The NYS Department of Motor Vehicles, the United States military, other entities mentioned, or persons refenced.

Dedication

I dedicate this book to God, my Guardian Angels, my wife Amy, my beautiful boys Anthony & Aidan, and our family dog "Legend." Thank you for your love and support!

To all those who perished in the attacks of 9/11. I honor you, I pray for you, and I pray for your families, friends, and loved ones. You are in my heart always.

Please also join me in dedicating this book to my fellow first responders, witnesses, local residents, and business owners who were impacted, or helped in the rescue and recovery efforts.

To all the rescue and recovery workers, to include (but not limited to) law enforcement, military, firefighters, emergency response officials, emergency medical personnel, utility workers, construction workers, city, state, and federal officials, volunteers from all over who worked and responded in some way to the events of 9/11 and those still serving today. I love you, and we appreciate everything you did for our nation.

Stay brave, stay committed, and never falter, remember we serve a mission greater than ourselves; we need you.

To my fellow New Yorkers, you are strong, resilient, and brave. Thank you for all you do.

To the those who dedicate their time to keep the flame of remembrance burning at our nation's memorials and especially those dedicated to 9/11 memorials. Thank you, we all appreciate you.

Lastly, I would like to dedicate this book to all the children of alcoholics and all those who have suffered at the hands of substance abusers. I am a child of an alcoholic, I know. So, stay strong, you will make it; there are many dedicated professionals ready to help; I have faith in you. You've can do it!

Introduction

The snow was falling heavy; the flakes were the size of small pillowcases. At least, it seemed that way to me when I was ten. My bicycle and I were inseparable; it went everywhere I went, like a Cowboy and his horse.

As I pushed my bike down the center of the street, the snow was accumulating fast. I could no longer peddle through the heavy 2-inch-thick caked layer of snow that rapidly built up over the past few hours. So, I jumped off, grabbed the handlebars, and started pushing.

I was making my way home that evening from a friend's house. We'd just finished watching our favorite movie, *Willy Wonka & The Chocolate Factory*. I swear we must have watched that movie a dozen times, every time it came on TV. It was magical and took us away to a beautiful place. Not to mention it always cost my mother money because we would ask her to buy half a dozen chocolate bars each time, we finished the movie. We imagined there had to be one more golden ticket still out there somewhere. Ahh, Dreams.

About halfway home while pushing, I paused in the middle of the street; it was dark already. A week before Christmas. Homes were adorned with a litany of Christmas lights. Through the big bay windows, I could see families were snug on their couches beside their fully decorated Christmas trees. I could see them drinking hot chocolate and watching family TV shows as they snugged under a warm comforter. I imagined what they must have felt, thinking *"We are safe, it's Christmas time, the best time of the year, and nothing could go wrong."*

The thought caused me to reflect about my own life. I'm out here braving the weather; not a big deal because it felt normal to be out in the elements with my bike. At the same time, my family was also home tucked in "warm by the fireplace."

Funny as it seemed, the street felt more like a natural place to me in some respects than my own home. I recall thinking how I would enjoy the job of a police officer, working in the streets to keep everyone safe. This way the rest of the community could stay home and warm under a comforter.

I didn't mind staying up late. I just wanted to be one who ensured their safety so they could make new memories together.

You know how they say, "It was that moment I knew"? Well, that was my moment. Something just clicked within me; I knew from that second, I wanted to work a job that would keep America safe.

Fast forward two years, I am about to finish 5th grade. My father walks in from work holding a brochure.

"Son, I have something I want you to look at."

"What's that, Dad?"

"New York Military Academy, a military college preparatory school in Cornwall, New York, just south of West Point. Grades 5 through 12. I thought you'd like to go here because you enjoyed the Young Marines?"

It only took about an hour after reading the brochure while staring up at the ceiling from my bed, thinking this would be perfect. I ran back downstairs and said yes.

That day, my father's forethought, and my decision to attend New York Military would chart a course and set the stage for my eventual career in law enforcement.

Who would've known?

The uniforms, the disciple, and the leadership environment provided just the right ingredients to manifest my desire and sculpt me for a career protecting America.

I had no idea what was ahead of me. No contemplation at all of how I would go about making my dream come true. But the feeling never waned. It took a few years after graduating the military school before things began to take shape.

Soon I would discover America!

Contents

Prologue

September 11, 2001

We were at war.

I was shaving right before I got the news. From my bathroom mirror, I could see the reflection of the television in the living room. Like most cops, I always turned on a morning news program before heading to work. It was hammered into me to "make sure nothing blows up before you head to work, politically or actually." Knowing what was happening before I left, the house had become a habit.

Usually, I would have already been at work by now. My office was on the sixth floor of Six World Trade Center. I was in the process of moving over sensitive undercover electronic equipment. Because it was so expensive, I had to do it by hand. But on this day, I was scheduled to work the swing shift. All the agents in my group had to undergo weapons training in Brooklyn that day.

To maintain our required firearms proficiency, we had to participate in a quarterly scheduled firearms training qualification each quarter. This particular quarter involved a variety of low-light simulations for shotguns set up by the firearms instructors. I had gotten in only a few hours before because I had been out all night conducting undercover surveillance, so I was wide awake that morning. But since we weren't starting until late in the day, I would get some much-needed rest after I shaved. I knew I had a long night ahead of me. So, I wanted to be fresh and awake. I'd be lucky to be home by midnight that day.

I rinsed my razor and put it away. Then I stretched my arms wide, yawning, basking in the sunny view of the morning light through my living room window.

Then suddenly, in a moment, everything in my world changed forever.

At first, the morning show broke into a report that a plane had crashed into the North Tower of the World Trade Center a few minutes earlier. I glanced at my watch.

8:51 a.m.

My wife should've finished with her sonogram and headed to her office by now. She started at nine, working for the U.S. Department of Labor. Her office was also on the sixth floor of Six World Trade Center—right down the hall from mine. It was at this moment, seeing smoke billow up from the North Tower, that my concern grew immensely.

Turning up the volume, I listened closely to the breaking news. Initial reports said it was a small plane that might have accidentally gone off course. I continued getting ready, keeping an eye on the TV.

I was putting my pants on when I heard that a United Airlines jet crashed into the South Tower. I saw replays of it over and over on every station. This sent my concern skyrocketing. I couldn't get dressed fast enough.

Taking a breath, I let my years of training overcome the panic rising in my chest. I stared at the clock in the kitchen.

9:11 a.m.

Who would know that this moment, this day, this specific time, would resonate in my life in ways far greater than I could have imagined?

I ran out to my balcony and leaned over the railing. Since my condominium was right on the Hudson River, I could see down the Hudson River and the smoke from both towers.

Immediately, I began gathering all the government-issued equipment in my apartment: my bulletproof vest, a shotgun, several handguns, and any other tactical gear I could locate. I wanted to have anything I could possibly need to deal with whatever nightmare was coming down from the sky.

Suddenly, my Nextel rang. It was my boss.

"The JTTF just contacted us. This is not an accident."

Joint Terrorism Task Force. Those dudes had to know the threat we faced.

"Tony, I need you to stay put until I call you back. Understand?"

"I was just getting ready to head down there," I protested.

"I need you to stay put. There could be a secondary attack, and we don't want any remaining law enforcement to rush into an ambush. Stay put until I call you back and give you the go. Got it?"

I looked down and, with my best war face, looked out the window and thought about it intensely. My military training and a life in law enforcement had taught me three concepts: expect the unexpected, head toward danger to protect lives, and seek those responsible. I needed to be downtown to help in any way possible.

"Tony, are you listening to me?"

Life in the military and law enforcement also taught me a fourth absolute: follow orders. I had no choice besides knowing my boss was right. Secondary attacks were something we really had to consider.

"Yes, sir. I'll stay put until you call back. But I'll still load up my van, so I'll be ready when you call back."

"Great. Bye."

When my wife drove up, I had just finished stuffing my undercover van with everything I could find. I couldn't reach her by cell phone because the cell towers were situated atop the trade center and had been disrupted by the attack. I rushed to hug her, embracing her like never before.

She told me she had been turning onto the street adjacent to Six World Trade Center, parked her car, and was crossing the street to head up the escalator when the second plane struck over her head. Debris had rained down but didn't harm her or the unborn son she was carrying.

"The doctor said the sonogram was normal. On the way home, I stopped at the supermarket and got cash from the ATM, $300.00, water, batteries, and all the canned goods I could grab. I also grabbed this small "crank up" radio. It was the only one left on the bottom shelves, figured you could use it. Here, bring some cash and food with you. I know you have to go."

Amy was the best. Always prepared and on the ball, and always thinking of others before herself.

My Nextel went off again.

Nextel cell phones we unique phones that worked as a cell phone combined with a built-in walkie talkie feature.

"Tony, get down here now! Bring everything you've got. We're gonna need it, and we're gonna turn that van into a communications platform."

"Yes, sir," I told him. "I'm almost loaded up."

I hurried my remaining trips to the van. During one return trip, I caught a glimpse of the TV. There were large plumes of smoke on the screen.

"The South Tower has just collapsed," the announcer said. I couldn't believe it. Stunned, I stood there watching the replays and the unfolding chaos.

"This is war," I told Amy. "No doubt about it."

"What are you going to do?"

"I'm going down there. I have my orders. Besides, those victims and my buddies need me,"

I made several more trips and returned for one last moment with my wife.

"You be careful, Honey. And check in with me."

I said, "Oh No! You are getting out of here! I need you somewhere safe."

I told her to grab her things and drive north as far as she could and to ensure she traveled over 90 miles away from Indian Point Nuclear Power Plant. I thought to myself that the plant could be another potential target.

My wife was pregnant with our first child, and I didn't want her anywhere near New York City or another possible target.

She fought me tooth and nail on that one, and refused to leave, but ultimately, I didn't have the time to argue; I had to go, and she insisted on being home when I returned.

I gave up that fight; I gave her a scared smile, nodded, and kissed her several times, not knowing if I would ever see her again.

Then I jumped in the van and took off.

Ten minutes into my trip, I was speeding down the West Side Highway. It was eerie. I was the only vehicle heading into New York City. Everyone else was coming out of the city.

At the end of the highway were several NYPD (New York City Police Department) checkpoints I had to go through. At around the last checkpoint just under the George Washington Bridge is roughly about the time when the North Tower fell. I couldn't believe what I heard on the radio.

In fact, I *didn't* think about it until I got closer and saw all the dust-covered executives walking toward me.

I glanced up toward the smoke-filled sky, trying to spot where the towers used to stand.

My new office is at Six World Trade Center. Is that still standing?

I raced down the Westside highway as fast as I could. I was the only vehicle heading south, so it was clear sailing. It didn't take much time to reach Broadway, near 26 Federal Plaza, where our other office was. The dust cloud was so thick I couldn't see where the World Trade Center towers once stood. Instead, I saw my friend Chris, a uniformed police officer. He was carrying a woman covered in dust and blood. I jumped out, helping him move her to safety.

After we helped her to the nearby lobby, there were some people enabling the wounded, so we ran back out to help as many other people as possible.

It looked like the end of the world.

People were running, screaming, and shouting in sheer terror and utter panic. I directed as many people to safety, calling, "This way, this run this way," as I pointed uptown away from the World Trade Center. I helped whoever needed assistance, which in fact, seemed like everyone.

After a while, my Nextel rang again. It was the boss.

"Tony! This is really bad. I need you to rally at the old office at 26. I need you to…"

His voice was suddenly cut off.

"Hello?" I said into the flip phone. "Hello? Are you still there?"

Chapter 1

"Loosen the tie, you're in."

January 1992

Hawthorne, New York

I pushed open the black metal gate to the entrance of the cemetery. Got back in my car and drove past the headstones, grave markers, and mausoleums.

The place was still. Quiet.

From my previous trips, I'd learned that The Gate of Heaven Cemetery closed the main entrance around dusk. Still, the gate was usually left half open after dark for those leaving late. The fading light cast shadows across the landscape, making for an excellent photograph or painting hanging on someone's wall—if it wasn't a place of death.

Halfway in, we parked the car.

"How far in is it?" Sammie asked.

"Not too far," I replied. "Are you scared?"

"No. It's just that I don't feel like walking five miles!"

I secretly grinned.

We continued over the winding sidewalk, passing the pine trees and bare sugar maples. It will be dark soon. I assumed that was why the cemetery was empty.

"Here it is," I said, pointing to the grave. "That's where my mother is buried."

"Man, one year ago. It's hard to believe she's gone," Sammie said.

"You saw what she went through. No one could survive that. The drinking took its toll on her liver and body."

"I guess you're right."

I said a quick prayer and crossed myself.

"Come over here," I said, pointing to a grave. "That's Babe Ruth's grave."

Sammie stared at the stone.

"Now he keeps your mother company, along with Billy Martin, James Cagney, Sal Mineo, and Houdini's wife, Bess."

We turned to leave.

"Say, listen," Sammie said as we walked. "I want to become a firefighter, so I'm going to take the test. You want to do it with me?"

I shook my head. "No way. I don't have any desire to become a firefighter. Besides, I can't get in. I don't have any relatives in firefighting to vouch for me. It's closed off to guys like me. You know how it works in New York City; you have to have a relative that was in before you to vouch for you."

"Come on," Sammie said. "I heard of some guys who don't have anyone who was a New York City Firefighter and are getting in. And hey, it's firefighting. Think about how cool that is."

I shook my head again. "I'd be wasting my time."

"Okay, but they're also giving the NYPD police test across the hall. You'd be a great police officer, especially after all you did at the New York Military Academy. You were a leader, a cadet officer. Now, you can be a leader in the real world and help keep our city safe."

"Hmm," I said, thinking about it. I was looking for something special, something challenging. My mentor Colonel Theodore R. Dobias, had always told me, "Make your mark on this world. Do something big." With the scars I carried from childhood, this might be the best way to heal while helping my fellow citizens. Besides I'd had a dream since that day pushing my bike through the snow, dreaming someday I would like to be a police officer.

"I'll do it, Sammie," I said as we cleared the gate. "You may have just changed my life."

***

Two months later, I received a letter in the mail. It was my score on the law enforcement test. I opened the envelope and found I'd got an extremely high score. Then, the calls followed.

The New York Police Department was recruiting me hard.

"I told you," Sammie said. "Are you going to take that job?"

"They haven't offered me anything official yet. Besides, I also took the U.S. Border Patrol test."

I had been reading The Chief, a civil service newspaper in New York City. During lunch, I occasionally stopped my soda truck, grabbed the paper at the newsstand, and furiously scanned the notice section for upcoming tests, like the Border Patrol. This was 1992, way before the Internet.

One day, I received a call from the New York City Police Department. "Okay, Tony," the man said, "we have you scheduled for the next class in June. But before we can guarantee a slot, we must perform an extensive background check."

"Great," I said. "Let me know when I need to do it; I'm in."

That call was immediately followed by the Border Patrol. "You've done well on the test; we'd like to interview you. Can you come to our office in lower Manhattan?"

"Sure," I said, surprised. "Just give me a date and time."

A week later, I sat in front of a seven-member Border Patrol Agent selection board—three to the left and three to the right. The leader sat directly before me at the far end of a very long table. It was intimidating, to say the least.

I smoothed out my suit and straightened my tie. They hadn't asked for a resume or any background. Thus, these board members didn't know anything about me other than my name and a referral sheet from the Justice Department.

The seven men were quiet, studying me. Not sure when this interview would start, so to prepare, I pulled out a pen and legal pad from my briefcase. That definitely got things rolling.

"Why did you bring a pen and paper to this interview?" the crusty old leader asked.

"I want to be prepared in case you give me instructions to do something, sir."

"That's fantastic!" he said, clapping his hands. His face looked positively jubilant.

"You're the only candidate who walked in with a pen and paper. That means you're prepared. Where did you learn that from?"

"Toujours pret. It's the motto of the military preparatory school I attended—New York Military Academy. It means always ready, always prepared."

I tossed in the name of my high school since famous people like Francis Ford Coppola, and Stephen Sondheim had gone there.

"That's unbelievable," he said, making way too big a deal about this. I decided to do something before he built a bronze statue of me.

"You know," I said, "the pen is your most important tool in law enforcement. It's as important as having your weapon. You can't do anything in law enforcement if you don't have a pen."

"That's right," he said. "No reports. No evidence. We might as well roll up the streets and go home. Let the criminals roam free."

I nodded, unsure if he was playing with me or perhaps just five years past his last competency exam.

"Okay, ready to go," he said, his hands slamming against the table. "I need some identification. Your name is Anthony, but how do I know who you are? You could be substituting for somebody else."

"Of course," I said. "Will a driver's license work?"

"Yeah, a driver's license works. But I need two forms of I.D."

I opened my wallet and pulled out my driver's license.

"What's that?" he asked loudly, pointing at a pink card emanating from my wallet.

"That's my work I.D. I have one for work and one for driving."

"No, that pink one. The pink one"

I pulled out the card and handed it to him. He passed it around to the six others.

After looking at the card, collectively they said, "Loosen your tie, relax, you're in good hands."

My military training had always taught me to keep my tie tight. So, I decided to leave it.

"Didn't I just give you a direction?" he said. "You'll never make a great Border Patrol Agent unless you know how to follow instructions."

"Yes, sir," I replied, adjusting it enough so he could see it was loose.

"Why don't you take a breather and go outside for a drink of water while we talk?"

"Yes, sir."

I stepped out into the hall, wondering if I was on a T.V. show, one where they filmed you doing stupid stuff. Either that or this was undoubtedly the oddest interview I'd ever attended.

As I wandered the hallway, I felt glad my Air Force Air National Guard card had been hidden just enough so a corner was peeking out. I didn't want to be a "buff"—a guy trying to show off my credentials. Because he'd had to pry it out of me, made me look better.

After a few minutes of looking for T.V. cameras, I wandered back in.

"You know why I told you to loosen your tie?" the leader asked.

"Because I was an honor graduate from the United States Air Force Security Police Academy. I was also a security policeman, he said. Do you know any Air Force Security Policemen?"

"Chuck Norris," I replied.

"Exactly!" he cried. "You've got four Chuck Norris's on this side of the table and three guys that were in the U.S. Army on this side. That means it's four against three."

I smiled and said nothing.

"Okay, Tony. Just answer these questions."

He posed a series of scenarios, and I gave him all the answers. After thirty minutes, he asked, "What are you doing for work right now?"

"I am a salesman for the Pepsi Cola Company. I have my own route, taking orders and making deliveries. I also have a "shaper" who works for me."

"What's a shaper?" the leader asked.

"He's the guy who gets the sodas off the truck and takes them to the customer while I walk to the shops to collect more orders."

"I see. How long have you been with Pepsi?"

"Six years."

"Six years!" he shouted, glaring at the three Army men. "That shows loyalty and stability. Good stuff!"

Actually, it showed intelligence. I was pulling in upwards of $87,000 a year with Pepsi. That was great money back in the late 1980's and early 1990's.

Along with the high income, I honored and respected Pepsi. Working for the company was fantastic. They treated me great. And I brought joy to many people when I delivered Pepsi and Pepsi products. I was eternally grateful for the opportunity they had given me.

However, I wanted to follow my heart and continue with what my military academy and the Air Force had prepared me to serve and protect my country. A call to public service was a perfect way to do just that. It seemed like this was my moment. Not to mentioned it aligned with my childhood dream of wanting to become a police officer.

"Anything else we should know?" he asked me.

There was so much he needed to hear. But there was no way he'd listen to it. I wasn't about to say anything about my childhood, my parents, or how, until recently, I had maintained custody of my younger brother while receiving three hundred dollars a month in child support from my dear old dad. Until now, my life had been fifty shades of messed up.

"No, sir," I told him. "Everything is great."

He reached across the table and shook my hand. "Welcome to the United States Border Patrol."

"Thank you, sir. You won't be sorry."

"I know I won't. Now, before you get too excited, the starting pay is $21,800 a year."

"Okay," I said, swallowing hard. I'd have to make some serious cutbacks.

"And one more thing. Many times, we'll drop you off near the border, maybe in a desert. You'll be all alone, with only your weapon and your wits."

"And his mighty pen," one of the Army men said, the smirk visible on his face.

"Right!" the leader said, either not picking up the sarcasm or ignoring it.

"You'll have a pen to scratch out your last words if you don't think smart. Can you handle that?"

"I can, sir." I assumed he was joking.

"Great. We'll send you a date to report."

I shook their hands and left.

As I walked out of the building, I recalled a recruiting sign I saw at the Air Force base when I had initially joined up with the New York Air National Guard. It said, "Careers take off with the United States Air Force."

It was at that moment I put it all together. My Air Force connections and street smarts landed me a job with the U.S. Border Patrol. I was on my way. Where I was going, I had no idea. But I hoped they would provide me with a compass. I was going to need it.

Chapter 2

"On the job",
Welcome to the US Border Patrol

I called NYPD and canceled my recruitment process. Then, I worked with Pepsi to hire a new person to take over my route. When everything was ready, I packed a few suitcases and hit the road.

I was excited about this opportunity. It was a multidimensional job. And I'd have a law enforcement certification once I graduated from the academy that I could take to any agency.

As the miles clicked by, I dreamed of climbing the law enforcement ladder just like I had done at New York Military Academy, traveling from a private to the Brigade Executive Officer, second in command, my senior year. I wondered what my career would look like when I was done.

The Immigration and Naturalization Service Border Patrol Academy was located in Artesia, New Mexico. Artesia is a small town about forty minutes south of Roswell, New Mexico. The Federal Law Enforcement Training Center, as it's called, is on the northwest side of town.

According to what I had been told, the government had purchased the former Artesia Christian College after foreclosure due to back taxes. It was then renovated into a training center. At the time, the complex was the entire footprint of the college, with a couple of new buildings erected to accommodate the influx of new students.

I flew to El Paso, Texas, and joined up with other recruits. We took a long bus ride through the desert with no air conditioning. It was a grueling trek. There was even a local farmer that hitched a ride along with his chicken.

When we arrived, we were greeted by high fencing and heavy security. The security officer examined the bus drivers' credentials and let the bus load of us in.

The bus pulled up in front of the dining hall. A Border Patrol Academy Drill Instructor boarded the bus, gave instructions, and we were told to exit the bus in an orderly fashion.

The Border Patrol was considered the Marine Corps of law enforcement. It garnered a reputation as the government's hardest law enforcement academy to get through. Its high washout rate was a testament to that fact. In most instances, less than half the class ever makes it. Their academy was as tough as Marine Corps boot camp.

I had studied the requirements prior to arriving and felt very confident I could get through it. After all, I'd already completed the Air Force's basic training and the Security Police Academy, graduating with honors. I planned on achieving the same here. I was motivated to get my career started.

The sixteen-week academy started off hard. Although the physical training was brutal. Long runs in the desert with heavy packs and little water were the norm. A "black flag" was raised when the temperature was too hot to train outdoors. This was supposed to happen a lot as days were mostly over 100 degrees. However, we rarely saw that black flag rise up the pole. That meant we were outside huffing in the desert heat. We didn't dare complain either.

The boots they issued were heavy. They were designed to protect us from thorns, desert scorpions, and snake bites. I worked on mine, finding ways to lighten them up. This allowed me to run faster than most others. I had to; I was elected to carry the class flag from the very start. That meant wherever we went as a class, I led the class platoon.

There was a great deal of book learning. We studied immigration and naturalization law, criminal law, constitutional law, police science...etc.

We read treatises on criminal law. We learned the statutes and their related court interpretations. The instructors covered all the Border Patrol procedures we needed to follow, most of which required using a pen. The academy tested us on all this material until we had it down. It involved many longs nights of staying up late with my desk lamp on, memorizing as much as possible before the big exams.

Another critical component of law enforcement is firing your weapon quickly and accurately. They had us at the range practically every day. We went through buckets of ammunition. Even though we had protection, my ears rang after every session. Gunfire is just something you have to get used to.

The target range requirements were different for our training. A traditional police academy routinely qualifies cadets at twenty-five yards (the farthest distance), as most gun battles occur in less than 100 feet. For us, the targets were set at fifty yards for the farthest distance.

We were required to qualify with a revolver and speed loaders to successfully complete the firearms training qualification to graduate. We were required to score three headshots and three body shots with each load. I had to speed load because there were many more targets than rounds in the revolver. And all this was timed. The U.S Border Patrol at that time was the only federal law enforcement agency to require their agents to qualify from fifty yards out.

It was tough. But I had to admit by the time I was done, I could hit what I aimed at, and I eventually qualified as a Sharpshooter.

Bill Jordan was the top shot in the United States Border Patrol for many years. He wrote a book, No Second Place Winner. He was considered one of the greatest marksmen in the U.S. during his time. While on patrol, he rode a horse. This guy was hardcore.

Later in life, I purchased one of Bill's books and framed it for my office along with a first-edition U.S. Border Patrol comic book. They are special possessions of mine.

Another huge component of getting through the academy was the ability to be proficient in the Spanish language. My teacher, Senior Agent Sanchez, pulled me aside one day to have a conversation. "Where did you learn Spanish?" he asked me.

"From working with my father. He owned a Coca-Cola franchise in New York. It came with a territory that he serviced. I worked for my father as a shaper or helper, shaping up, as we called it, on the truck for years."

"A what?"

"Dad went into these bodegas (Spanish Delis) and larger markets and took the orders. He gave me the written customer invoice, and I delivered the soda. It was hard work, but I started learning the language. Eventually, he wanted me to learn Spanish. So, he sent me into Bodega's to take the orders for beverage products in Spanish. Whatever sales I made; I earned an extra profit. It was great motivation to learn a second language."

"Did you take any in school?"

"In the tenth grade, I wanted to take Italian as an elective because my father's side of the family is from Italy. However, my father insisted I take Spanish. He said, 'That's going to become a second language here in our country sooner than you think. That's how you're going to get a job. You learn Spanish,' he said constantly."

"And did you follow his advice?"

"Yep. I listened to him and learned it. When I returned to the shops to take orders for Coca-Cola, I could speak Spanish better each time. This increased sales, and I was able to save for my first car too."

"Well, Tony, I hate to tell you, but you still need a lot of work. You're going to be put into situations where you're alone. You'll be pursuing a large group of illegal aliens through scrub brush, and you won't be discussing Coca-Cola products.

You may apprehend three or four of them, but it could get extremely dangerous if you're not careful. You need to know more than what it takes to receive an order for Coca-Cola in Spanish."

"I understand," I said. "The truth is, if a suspect wants to order a soft drink, I can tell him the sizes, flavors, and costs. If I need him to throw up his hands or turn around, I'm screwed."

He laughed. "Don't worry. When you graduate, you'll be bilingual. It's required (the U.S. Border Patrol at the time was the only law enforcement agency in the United States where speaking Spanish was a requirement to maintain your job). Trust me, I'm going to immerse you in Spanish."

He did. The last month of the academy was all Spanish. No English was spoken. We were out of luck if we couldn't articulate it in Spanish. We wore large buttons for a week that said, "No Ingles." This meant the other students in the classes behind us, and the staff were not permitted to talk to us in English.

I must admit that when I completed this academy, I was in the best physical condition of my life. My Spanish was incredible, and I had tremendous confidence in my knowledge and abilities. They did a fantastic job preparing me for the rugged world of law enforcement in the Border Patrol.

On graduation day in October 1992, I received my certificate, badge, and gun. Sammie sent a letter congratulating me. He had also landed a public service job and would eventually retire with a great pension.

Before I left, Senior Agent Sanchez joined me for a beer at the local watering hole.

"I want to give you some unsolicited career advice," he said. "Are you up for it?"

"Of course. Let me hear it, sir."

"Working for the federal government means lower pay than the private sector. But in federal law enforcement, the pay is even worse."

"I see that."

"You'll risk your life for pennies on the dollar while some guy in a suit sits at a desk out earning you. But one benefit the federal government has besides lots of holidays is the retirement check. To get the check, though, normally, you must endure thirty years. Now, here's the good news: law enforcement only has to put in twenty years to get the check. That is if you're still alive. Understand?"

"I do."

"Now, let me go over the important numbers you need to focus on."

He explained that the biggest number I needed to think about during my career was the average of my highest three consecutive years of salaries. When I retired, the government would look for that number, say $100,000. Then they would take 1.7 percent—or $1,700—and multiply that by the years of service—twenty. Then you add your social security annuity and Thrift Savings Plan (401K equivalent), and you have your total retirement check. Administrative workers used a 1 percent figure instead of 1.7 percent, which meant they had to work 30 years to have a halfway decent retirement.

"So, Tony, the more years you put in, the higher your salary, the higher that check becomes."

"Okay. I guess that's something to look forward to."

"Yeah, but here's the best advice I can give you—ready?"

"Sure," I said. "Do I need to brace myself?"

"You might if you don't follow it. The big piece of advice is this: You must always be looking to move up in pay. Always. If you grow complacent, you'll retire with nothing."

I nodded, taking a sip of my beer.

"Always keep an eye on the notices for open federal jobs," he added, pointing his longneck at me. "Even if you have to leave the Border Patrol someday. It's sad to be a job hopper or gypsy, as we sometimes say, but the federal system somewhat encourages it. You cannot wait for the person above you to move on or die. You must make a move yourself, always climbing up the pay scale ladder."

I listened to and absorbed everything he said. Later, I'd learn to value his advice more than he would ever know.

Thank you, Agent Sanchez!

***

Six months later, with the academy over, we received our commissions, badges, duty weapons, and assignments. The Border Patrol sent me to their premier California station in San Clemente, California. One of my responsibilities was working with my Senior Agent Patrol Agent. Our first assignment was to patrol around President Nixon's home, which was nearby. President Nixon lived in San Clemente, right next to a power plant. It was an easy assignment compared to what I had expected.

My first few weeks also found me hiding in the trunks of cars. I was bait for the dogs to find. New Agents were addressed as "trainees" according to the Senior Agent fraternity; we didn't warrant being called Agents until we passed the 14-month-long probation period. They often used Trainees for dirty jobs around the stations, such as having us hide in trunks so the K-9 dogs could practice sniffing us out.

Each time they put me in a nasty old trunk of a seized car we had out back in the pound, I was greeted by a snarling German Shepherd and laughing Senior Agent when the truck lid opened. By this point, I wasn't feeling much like a law enforcement officer.

Besides guarding a former President's home, I worked at a checkpoint. The Border Patrol would stop random vehicles on the freeway, allowing us to conduct formal immigration inspections.

Unlike a typical police-citizen encounter on the streets of any city, at the time, the U.S. Supreme Court allowed us to inspect people and vehicles with little to no probable cause because it was considered an extension of the border. Essentially, the same as a point of entry at the border into the United States. Of course, we didn't have the manpower to inspect everyone, so we had to have reasonable cause to inspect a vehicle.

It was late October in southern California. The sun came out from behind a thin layer of clouds, its hot rays biting the back of my exposed neck. For what seemed like the thousandth time in the long hours I'd been standing on the highway.

I sometimes wondered what I was doing here. I was so far from where I had grown up.

Even though I'd been on the job for less than thirty days, my career suddenly felt like it was going nowhere. I had joined the U.S. Border Patrol to serve my country but had been told of the incredible stories of action and excitement. Everyone had told me,

"You'll be in places alone. All you'll have is your weapon, your ability to speak Spanish, and your brain. There could be a dozen or so bad guys ready to surround you. You'd better rely on your training to survive."

I had eaten it up. Yet after enduring that grueling academy, I was standing on the hot pavement of the San Clemente Border Station, a secondary stop for smugglers located just east of I-5. Every day, I watched the endless stream of cars crawl by, each passing through my personal inspection.

Where was the action? The excitement?

Not here, that's for sure.

I glanced at my watch. It was barely three in the afternoon. I still had another three hours until quitting time.

Man, how long am I going to take this? I thought to myself.

The next car—a maroon Chrysler New Yorker—inched to a stop in front of my partner. Like the last five hundred times, I walked over to the driver and tapped on the window. "Please turn off the engine. State your citizenship, please," I said.

When he didn't understand, I repeated the question in Spanish.

"Mexican, I am from Mexico" he replied in Spanish as he cut the engine.

"Where are you headed?"

"To work in Los Angeles."

"Who do you work for?" I asked.

"McCormick's. We make spices."

I shielded my eyes from the sun as I peered into the backseat. It was clean. Way too clean.

"Where did you come from?" I asked.

"San Diego," the driver replied.

"Why were you in San Diego?"

He hesitated as if remembering the proper answer. "My sister was sick. I was visiting her."

"Where does your sister work?"

He licked his lips and hesitated again. "On Wilshire Boulevard."

Wilshire Boulevard was a famous road in Los Angeles. I didn't know San Diego well, but I highly doubted they had the same road running through their city.

My twenty-six days' worth of on-the-job experience kicked in at that moment, telling me something wasn't right. I moved my head, giving my partner a sign. His eyes opened wide. This was the first time I'd given him our secret signal. Unfortunately, he was just as inexperienced as me. He took a few steps to get a better view through the passenger window while I made the next move.

"Sir, are you carrying any illegal contraband?" I asked nonchalantly as my heart skipped a beat in my chest.

"No," he said, his eyes shifting away from me.

I pointed to the car's hood. "Can I look under your hood and in your trunk?"

"Si," he said eagerly, popping the hood.

I moved around to the front, clicking on my flashlight and examining the engine compartment. Satisfied there was nothing there, I left the hood up and moved back to the driver's side.

"Can I show you something?" I asked. It was always better to have him out of the car, away from any firearms, especially since I was about to move to the rear of the vehicle—where drugs or contraband could be hidden.

"Sure," he said, practically bolting from the car.

I pointed to a hunk of plastic bolted to the side of the engine compartment. "Is any contraband hidden behind there?"

"No," he said, shaking his head and smiling.

"Please stand on this side so my partner can see you."

I positioned him on the right front panel of the Chrysler while I walked back to the driver's side and popped the trunk. When I saw my partner tense up, that told me the suspect was tensing up. Putting my hand on my revolver, I eased back as I lifted the trunk with two fingers.

I watched the lid slowly rise, revealing clear plastic wrapped around a large brown square. Looking at it closer from the side, I confirmed my first thought. I had just caught a big fish, namely one large bale of weed.

"Marijuana, partner," I called out.

I couldn't see him, but I knew my partner was keeping his right hand on his revolver while motioning for the driver to put his hands on the hood. I cautiously continued around the side of the Chrysler. There, I spotted another large bale of marijuana next to the first one. They had both been crammed in the trunk, yet a gap existed between them. I stood fully at the rear bumper and studied this. Something was wrong.

Between the bales were VHS tapes and a lot of blood. Inching closer, I pushed some videotapes out of the way and saw a bloody face with eyes peering back at me. I tactically stepped back from the car to draw my weapon.

"Cuff him, partner!" I called out before I got shot by the stranger in the trunk.

Ripping my gun out, I aimed it toward the face. I stepped forward to force the person to come out, but they didn't move.

Adrenaline raced through me as I worked to control my breathing. I reached in with my free hand and took hold of their arm. I helped them out of the trunk and over to a bench where we had a secondary inspection area.

I signaled the alarm, and Border Patrol Agents came running from everywhere. We placed the driver into custody and got medical attention for the man in the trunk. Then we continued searching the vehicle, finding a .45 handgun and several VHS films. Each tape was filled with unique pornographic material. These were super valuable on the street, bringing in large sums of money—possibly more than marijuana.

It turned out my first bust was a major case. The guy in the trunk was an insider who would testify against the other bad guys. Unfortunately, they'd gotten to him first, and he nearly lost his life.

The driver admitted he was headed to L.A. to smuggle the drugs and tapes and was supposed to turn over the turncoat to his connection. Perhaps the bad guys in L.A. wanted to know what he knew first, but I can't be certain.

The Senior Agents above me made their "bones" on this case. Meaning they were credited with doing an excellent job in the eyes of their boss. They were set for a while.

I got a lot of pats on the back, but then it was back to work right away. I'd have to find another way to make my bones. Needless to say, though, I now had my action.

Life in the Border Patrol was about to take off.

Chapter 3

"Warrior Mindset"

One strategy they taught us in the academy was to constantly have a *"warrior mindset."*

When you're a warrior, you live life differently. If you're at a restaurant, you pick a booth that gives you a clear field of view of any trouble potentially coming your way. You always sit with your back against a wall. If you're walking to your car, you're looking around for trouble. You may even circle your vehicle once or twice before getting in to see if anyone is watching you.

In a movie theater, you sit in the back row, count the exits, and note their location.

After a while, it becomes second nature; and it seems as though you put less effort into it. The practices become part of your life routine.

Now to others, you may seem paranoid or "overprotective," but unfortunately, in today's world, it's almost imperative.

I have always said, "If you're not being paranoid, you're not paying attention."

Now I don't really mean practicing being paranoid; the phrase tends to grab someone's attention which is why I say that. What I really mean is to have your "antenna's up" and "head on a swivel."

Be alert and informed of your surroundings, your environment per se, and current events. By doing so, you're one step ahead of the game. Thinking like a warrior and acting like a professional.

Because I'm always carrying a weapon—even off duty—I must be mindful and safe, yet always ready to act. Safe for the others around me and myself. The longer you're in law enforcement, the more history you have. Some bad guys might want revenge. I guess that's why we have good retirement plans.

The truth is, when maintaining a warrior mindset, I'm never truly relaxed. I can't be. It's a practice of always "being" aware and consistently playing out scenarios in your mind. Asking yourself, if something bad happened right now, what would I do?

One example, for instance, was when I was on patrol in San Juan, Capistrano. I spotted what appeared to be a group of individuals conducting landscaping work. When I tried to stop and question them, they all ran in various directions.

Running from a uniformed law enforcement officer is considered probable cause for detention and potential arrest. Running at the sight of a green uniformed U.S. Border Patrol Agent usually means you are illegally within the United States.

So, I couldn't chase all of them, having to pick just one; I set out as fast as I could. I pursued a male who was in his mid-twenties age-wise. He ran into a laundromat. I pursued him, running up to its entrance, I began to think, "What just happened?" he suddenly disappeared into thin air. I knew for sure I just saw him run into the front entrance of the laundromat, but then "puff" like magic, and he was gone.

The people in the laundromat looked at me like I was from outer space. They indicated they had not seen anyone run in there.

"Come on now, I know I didn't just imagine it," I thought.

So, I started looking around, checking the bathroom first. That was the only place he could've gone, I thought.

"Nope, not there," so I continued to look around.

As I was about to give up, one person who was doing laundry and folding her clothes gave me the "nod" towards one of the machines. I walked over and opened the dryer and looked inside. Judging from the size of the tumbler, it might be possible for a small man to fit inside. I checked the empty ones and found nothing.

I walked to the exit and noticed a woman, her back to me, jealously guarding a dryer. I asked her to step aside. As my attention was focused on her, the door swung open, and out popped the suspect. My warrior mindset saved me. I was ready for anything at that point.

I looked at him and said, "Really? You're gonna get hurt in there. Come on."

Then I radioed for assistance. I asked him if he had entered the country illegally, and he openly admitted he did.

My team searched the laundromat but didn't find anyone else. It was a good lesson for me: Always be ready for anything because anything is always possible.

***

My time on interior patrol put me in increasingly dangerous situations. On another occasion, just like I'd been told in training, I found myself chasing a group of illegal aliens. As they spread out, one suspect jumped a picket fence into someone's backyard. I followed him.

Taking long strides, I eventually gained on him. He snuck a peek to see how close I was while attempting to jump over a white picket fence in a resident's backyard. It was at that moment he tripped, going over, falling face down.

I took the fence in one leap and was right on top of him. He tried to regain his balance and stand up, but I grabbed him at his waist, and we both went back down together. Fortunately, I landed on top. I was now behind him, trying to cuff him, when I heard a woman from a second-story window in front of me scream in Spanish, "Look out!"

I whipped my head around, only to see a man with a giant monkey wrench swinging for my head. I ducked. Grabbing my gun. In one motion, I spun around with my gun hand (my other hand holding the one cuff I managed to place on my suspect), and I aimed at his head, yelling for him to drop it. Fortunately, he complied.

I re-holstered so I could get back to cuffing my suspect beneath me when the same individual came around to the side of me and slammed his fist into the side of my head, nearly knocking me out. He punched me so hard; I began to see stars.

Before I knew what was happening, a large crowd had formed. My partner arrived just in time, saving me from an extremely dangerous situation. I escorted my prisoner toward the van. Walking him

35

through a resident's backyard with literally dozens of shouting protesters, all with sticks and rocks.

I reached the van, where my partner helped me load my prisoner with the others.

By now, the crowd had moved to our van and were trying to tip it over. If you think about it, it was a good strategy on their part. The crowd had sized up the odds, two of us and about fifty of them at this point.

There were already twelve prisoners inside. They must have figured that if we couldn't leave, neither could the prisoners.

That's when our backup arrived; they helped locate the individual who punched me. We arrested him and transported him to the station. Needless to say, we got out of there by the Grace of God.

The suspect I caught was deported to Mexico, and the individual who attempted to kill me with the monkey wrench and later punched me in the head received significant jail time. The rest were processed and released back to Mexico, despite knowing more than likely they would all return again the next day. We saw certain people so often we just laughed and processed them repeatedly, knowing many of them on a first-name basis. It was an interesting way to secure the border.

After the ordeal with the wrench, and after our shift was over, my partner and I were enjoying a beer when he asked me, "Are you thinking about what would have happened if you'd got hit with that monkey wrench?"

"Not really. When I was a kid, my alcoholic mother chased me around the yard drunk with an ax handle on a number of occasions, so suffice to say, unfortunately, I'm a little used to it."

"What was she trying to do?"

"I don't know, but she certainly wasn't flagging me down to wish me happy birthday. Actually, I told him, on one occasion, it was because I refused to testify against my father in their divorce hearing. So, she was so angry at me that she wanted me to leave our home. The only problem was I was only a senior in high school, and I had nowhere else to go."

"That's terrible," he said.

"You get used to it. In an eerily strange way, though, growing up with a mother who was an alcoholic helped prepare me for this role and helped me be better conditioned when it comes to my warrior mindset."

***

My interior patrol of the surrounding towns was interrupted with more time at the highway checkpoint. Apparently, several agents had taken vacation while a few others were sick. Of course, it was the divisional round of the NFL playoffs. But I'm sure that had nothing to do with it.

My partner and I started the day processing the endless streams of cars, hoping to be the one Agent who stopped a major crime that day. It was hot, climbing up to 87 degrees by 2 p.m. We had sweat patches under our arms.

I was wiping the back of my neck with a bandana when my partner motioned for a car to come over to our secondary inspection area.

"Please state your citizenship," he said to the male driver. We were immigration officials first and foremost, so all inspections had to begin with first determining citizenship.

I looked inside and saw a female Hispanic passenger holding a child in a blanket. She gently rocked it to make sure it didn't cry.

I scanned the backseat, where a collection of stuffed animals was arranged. When I saw this was a rental car, that clued me in. Drug Mules will often pose as married couples, and they frequently use rental cars so that if they are caught, they don't lose their own vehicle during the seizure process.

My partner tapped on the roof, getting my attention to look up and over the car at him. "Baby's not moving," he mouthed.

I looked back down at the child. "Ma'am, please step out of the car."

She snapped her eyes at the driver. It was clear she didn't want to give up the baby or step outside.

"The baby is sleeping," she told me in Spanish.

I brought out a Border Patrol K9 dog and walked it around the car. The dog "hit on" it several times. Meaning it detected the presence of narcotics. This now meant we had probable cause to believe there were drugs in the car, and they might be smuggling drugs.

"Ma'am, please step out of the car," I said again.

I then ordered the driver out. Neither of them wanted to comply. We became more assertive, and then the woman complied and set her baby down. Slowly, she got out of the vehicle.

Eventually, the driver exited too. Once we had them both cuffed, my partner inspected the baby.

My partner told me that he had seen far too many cases where smugglers use deceased babies purchased in Mexico and then use the body to hide drugs. Then attempting to "mule" them past our checkpoints.

My partner felt the infant was suffering from severe trauma and called medical services. After inspecting the stuffed animals lined up in the back seat posing as toys for their child, we found all of them stuffed with cocaine.

Seeing scenes like that tended to stick with you for a while. For me, I found solace in exercise. Not only did I keep in shape, but the feelings of exhaustion from running five miles with a pack carried me through all the missed monkey wrenches and cocaine-stuffed baby toys.

If I needed a boost, I went to church, where I sat to be with God for a while. I might even talk with a priest. For sure, I prayed for those I encountered and those affected.

Unfortunately, the kryptonite of law enforcement is alcohol. That's the go-to solution for some cops. They called it "choir practice," a time to tell stories and receive some liquid therapy.

When I had a midnight shift, I had a few drinks with my partners at the local pub afterward. We'd talk over the day and decompress.

Over time, I found myself eating two hamburgers and drinking a pint at eight o'clock in the morning. Not good because, with severe alcoholism running in my family, I had to watch it. No way I was going to fall into that trap.

I soon put an end to the early morning breakfasts, replacing them with a regular exercise routine. A much better way to decompress.

***

There was a lot I learned during my time in the Border Patrol. Our station commander conducted random timed checkpoint inspections every Friday evening. It was a good time to do it because the smugglers assumed we were either shorthanded or on interior patrol.

Shortly before I arrived at the station from the academy, there was a high-speed chase where the Border Patrol chased a vehicle that failed to stop for agents. The chase originated at the Temecula California Border Patrol checkpoint. It sadly ended in a horrific crash involving a school bus. Since then, pursuits both on foot and on the highways followed much stricter guidelines for safety.

So much so that California motioned the Border Patrol not to arrest illegal aliens on the freeways or highway medians. However, it didn't take long before the illegal aliens learned that if they could make it to the freeway median, they were safe and untouchable all the way north to Oregon.

To ensure the safest practices were in place, the goal was to stop them before they could hit the highway.

Over time, we did a great job and safely intercepted scores of smugglers. To the extent that I eventually became so confident I was able to arrest fifteen suspects at one time without any handcuffs. That's what we call using "Command Presence" and affiliated control techniques.

I encountered a lot of peculiar things during my time with the Border Patrol. One was a tactic used by illegal aliens to avoid getting caught.

Late one afternoon, I was chasing a male as he ran into the tall grass. For some reason, he suddenly stopped and dropped down into a crouching position. Seeing him curled up and tucked up with his knees against his chest, I slowed as I approached him, nervous about this strange development.

From past experience, I knew Mexico was a knife culture. The majority of illegal suspects we caught were from Mexico, and just about everyone we caught carried a knife, big or small. Concerned about this, I circled the suspect, approaching from the side.

I came close and tapped him on the shoulder.

He slowly opened his eyes and looked up. "Okay, officer, you got me," he said with a big smile. I just nodded my head and laughed for a brief second.

Once I secured him, I said, "Why did you just stop and sit down like that?"

He told me that in the Mexican culture, everyone believes that if you can't see a Border Patrol Agent, the Agent can't see you. Legend had it that hiding in the grass—no matter how high—worked best. It was like asking someone if they were a cop, believing that by law, they had to tell you.

Just as strange but even more so was one of the funniest things I ever saw happen during a foot pursuit when I was chasing a suspect. This pursuit started as a car chase and ended up on the beach, fairly close to the checkpoint in San Clemente. I had already jumped out of my cruiser and could see the suspect frantically weaving between beachgoers.

I was staying locked on him visually.

Then, all of a sudden, he grabs a surfboard from an unsuspecting surfer and starts to pretend he is a surfer. His frantic running around immediately slowed down to a way "cool surfer shuffle" through the sand as though he hadn't just been running from the Border Patrol five minutes ago. He had been there all day at the beach, headed back out for some more "tasty waves." As Sean Penn would say from Fast Times at Ridgemont High.

Honestly, I was doubled over laughing; a pretty good one; nice move. I gave him 10 points for originality. Regardless of how creative he was, I still couldn't let him go. So, I slowly crept up from behind and tapped him on the shoulder. Boy, the look on his face was hysterical; he did a good job trying to convince me he was a surfer.

Needless to say, his aspiring surfer career was over, and I didn't book the surfboard into evidence. We gave it back to the surfer he took it from.

***

Catching the same person over and over again was part of the job. But veteran Border Patrol Agents still considered us trainees until we had caught the same illegal alien twice on the same day. Don't ask me why; it was a fraternal thing with these old school Agents.

I could never figure it out, but it was most likely because we didn't graduate from the academy with them, so we'd never be fully accepted.

One day, I was performing a bus check. This involved me walking down the aisle of each passenger bus that was diverted off the highway so we could inspect the bus for illegal aliens or contraband being smuggled up from the border. I began all my checks determining citizenship first. When I hit the middle of the bus, a male shifted his body away from me, refusing to make eye contact. This is usually an immediate indicator when there's a problem. Avoidance behavior is a big clue.

Kinda like when you found the stash of milk chocolate your mother was hiding in the back of the pantry behind the cooking oil located way up on the top shelf. You know that bag of mini chocolates she saved as a surprise when you did good on a math test? Then she hunted you down when she figured out you found it? Only you'd never done well on the test, but now you have melted chocolate all around your lips, and your hands are suspiciously behind your back holding the wrappers, yet you still deny it. You know, like that.

Only in law enforcement we call that a "clue."

I came up to him and said, "Please state your citizenship," then asked, "Where were you born?"

"U.S. city," he replied.

"What high school did you go to?"

"U.S. high school."

Really, I thought. I know of no "U.S. city" or "U.S. high school, " so that would be two clues right off the bat.

"Stand up for me, please," I said in Spanish.

He complied.

I told him to keep moving to the rear of the bus so I could finish conducting my immigration inspections with the rest of the passengers.

When I finally made it to the back of the bus, and as he saw me coming, he bolted into the bathroom and attempted to dive out the tiny little bathroom window. I radioed outside to my partner, who found him hanging there, stuck half in, half out of the tiny bus window. Since we were at a Border Patrol station, he wasn't going anywhere.

Once we got him out, I processed him. I learned his name was Tito. After completing his paperwork, he was deported on the next bus back to Mexico. Funny, though, when I caught him the very next day at the checkpoint, we'd share a laugh about his attempted escape out the window, and I told him he had helped me. He said "How?"

I said thanks to you, I was now out of the "trainee" club!

"Those were the good times," I'd say.

"Ellos estaban seguros," he'd reply. They sure were.

Tito was a good person; ultimately, like most of the individuals I encountered from Mexico, they were just coming to the United States to earn a living for their families back in Mexico. They were good, hard-working, and religious people, and I always treated them with the utmost respect and dignity. I just wish I hadn't encountered them the way I did.

***

In January 1993, I'd been with the Border Patrol for over nine months when the Los Angeles County Sheriff's Department contacted us for help. They'd been arresting a large number of illegal aliens, most of whom didn't speak English; they spoke Spanish. These individuals, mostly illegal aliens, were tying up their jails. The Sheriff's Department wanted to turn them over to the immigration service quicker, or at least download criminal information, so they knew what they had.

My supervisor told me about a Border Patrol detail involving going to Los Angeles to help out. I asked if I could go but learned I was last on the list due to seniority. You know, the whole trainee thing. The Senior Agents got to go first.

But I wanted to see what type of work the Sheriff's Department did. I was flirting with the idea of possibly taking a job as a Deputy Sheriff. Undeterred, I called up there and asked if I could go on a ride-along as a guest officer on my days off. To my surprise, they agreed. They needed help.

I was assigned to a seasoned sheriff's deputy the first day- a Friday. I told him I had applied with his department when I was in New York but hadn't heard anything. I mentioned I was still interested in possibly joining the department if things didn't work out with the Patrol.

"Let's see if you like the work first," he said prophetically.

By the time we climbed into his patrol car and booted up this large computer on the dashboard, we were thirty minutes behind in calls.

"Man, you're busy," I said, looking over all the calls.

"It's like this every day. We need to prioritize them. Here's one—a shooting job. Let's go on that one." He used the term "job" instead of call.

We arrived to find other units had already responded, so we crossed it off and moved to the next one.

Like orders stuck on a diner's wheel, we worked our way through the jobs, finally reaching the nuisance calls. Once we were clear, we pulled into a deli and ordered some sandwiches. It was around 5 p.m.

"We have to eat standing up," he said. "If a high-priority call comes in, we drop the food and run. At least it keeps the weight off."

I thought we were busy with the Patrol. But this was insane.

We finished our food, making it back to the car just in time to catch up on another job. A nearby liquor store had been robbed. Incredibly, we picked up the suspect's car right in front of us; he made a wide turn hitting another parked car at our deli, nearly striking our patrol unit. We leaped into our unit and found ourselves immediately locked in a high-speed chase.

Ripping through the city, I gripped every part of the patrol car, holding on like a bull rider on top of old Diablo. When the suspects took an offramp, the extra speed going downhill caused them to lose control. Their car hit a fire hydrant, flipped over, and they bailed out.

My partner and I combed the area, splitting up to find these guys. A few minutes into it, I nabbed one of them in a dumpster. By the time I'd made it back to the patrol car, my partner had caught the other suspect at a gas station. We transported them to jail and hit the road again. According to him, it was just another wild night in L.A.

***

After some sleep, I showed up Saturday afternoon for round two. And it was the same drill. Behind on jobs from the start, racing from place to place to cross them off.

After hours of chaos, we found ourselves back at the same deli.

We were talking to the store owners, mentioning that we had just come from a crazy call, when the high pitch of tires squealing punctuated the air. We looked outside to see a Mustang on two wheels crashing into another car in the deli's parking lot. We dropped our sandwiches and ran to help. "You've got to be kidding me," I said, "twice in the same place and the very next day; who's gonna believe this?"

In this instance, the suspect was not about to cooperate. He jammed his damaged car into reverse and took off. We sprinted to the patrol car, hit the lights, and the chase was on.

After several blocks, he stopped at a red light, suddenly deciding to obey the traffic laws. Something was really weird here, I thought.

"I'll go get him," I said to my partner as I swung the door open.

I ran up to the old Mustang and surprised the driver. This was strange since we had the lights and siren on.

Using a special technique similar to a rodeo move, I held the driver back against the seat with my right hand while shutting off the engine with my left. In one smooth movement, I safely removed him from the car while cuffing him before my partner could even get out of the vehicle.

"Tony," my partner said, "we need to get you working for us."

At that moment, I felt I was really protecting the public from harm. This driver could've killed someone had we not stopped him. Yet, I didn't know it, but the night was far from over, and I had a lot more work ahead of us.

The bill I had punched when I first chose to become a law enforcement officer was about to be cashed.

On the way to jail with our fleeing drunk driver, we received a call. A gang shooting is in progress. Someone from the jail met us outside, grabbed the suspect, and we banked a U-turn out of the station.

Dodging traffic, we arrived at the parking lot of a popular fast-food restaurant. I could immediately see a great number of cars in the parking lot had been sprayed with bullet holes. People were screaming, crying, and running in every direction. It was complete pandemonium.

Being the first ones on the scene, we drew our guns and checked everything out. We quickly learned that a rival gang had conducted a "drive-by" with machine guns and shot everything at a four-foot level—the typical height of a drive-by shooting. The kids, sitting on the trunks eating sandwiches—had had their legs riddled with bullets. Blood was everywhere.

"Over here. Hurry!" someone yelled at me.

I ran to the voice and found a young man, a rival gang member, a teenager who couldn't have been older than 17 or so. He was on his back, his head resting on a curb. He had been shot in the chest several times but was still alive. I dropped to my knees and started first aid as the boy gasped for air.

We pulled up his shirt and could see several flaps in his chest squirting out blood. I had to do something fast.

I grabbed some nearby plastic bags and tried covering up the holes.

"You're going to make it," I said as I worked feverishly. "Come on, you're going to make it!"

Tears streamed from his young eyes and those huddled around him.

"Stay with me!" I yelled. "Just stay with me!"

The public began to gather around, watching, and some were helping assist. One woman said, "He's going to die. He's going to die."

I used all my training to try and save his life. I just knew I had a miracle in me.

The kid squeezed my hand and stared directly into my eyes. He continued gasping for air. At that moment, I could see his soul.

"You're going to make it," I said calmly. "I know for certain you're going to make it."

I closed my eyes and said a prayer just as the EMTs rolled up.

Chapter 4

I'll be back, man down

I sat on the train, staring out the window at the darkness racing by. I headed back to New York to check on my father. He was sick again and needed help. The Border Patrol had graciously given me some time off.

Even though it had been a week, I couldn't get that boy's face out of my mind. I still felt the squeeze of his hand as his chest rose and fell for what was to be the last time. His eyes remained open, but the tears stopped. The EMT's later told us that he had succumbed to his wounds.

The academy instructors talked about desensitization in professions such as law enforcement, where bad scenes are typical. A law enforcement officer must carefully process their thoughts to properly do this job.

"You can't inject your emotions because you must look at things differently."

"Seek facts and preserve evidence."

"It's just business."

They gave it to us straight.

But I found it tough in this instance. I was beside myself when I found out the boy had died. I still get emotional thinking about it. How can you not?

The victim was a gang banger. You could put a bandana on this young man and call him whatever you want, but he was still just a boy. He was a mother's son.

I tried to think about something else, like my father.

Born in 1940, Anthony "Sonny" Losito grew up in New York. He was an excellent athlete, pitching for Iona Prep in Westchester County. "A fastball faster than Bob Feller," the sports reporters wrote when he was a senior in high school.

When my father graduated high school, he was in talks to potentially be drafted by the Cleveland Indians; he was that good. Unfortunately, it never worked out; according to him, he was forced to stop talks having to return home when his father fell ill who later died of a heart attack. He now found himself having to support his mother and sister. It was both a professional and personal turn that would lead him to take another road.

This is where I step back, take a deep breath, and remove the emotions. As I've mentioned, there were no computers or the Internet back then. Men, desperate to impress other men, would say they had played ball for the Yankees. Or been in the farm system for the Dodgers. It was a safe lie because no one had the resources to check whether it was true.

As someone who makes a living sifting fact from fiction, it's hard to believe that a pitcher better than Bob Feller could not find a solution to playing while helping his father simultaneously. And what about the other teams? Don't you think a year or two later, someone would come knocking, like Cleveland? After all, they had blown a draft pick. That team might want some value for it.

But the story Dad told was one week of unhittable fastballs, and his career was over.

I had to run with what he told me; trust me, you never really got much from my father. He spoke less than a mime.

Now, finding myself in a similar scenario; as the firstborn, it was my job to take care of my father, no matter what I thought. At least he didn't have to pay me child support any longer. That uncomfortable barrier was removed.

My attention came back to the train and fear. I hated to admit it, but I was afraid of flying. That was why I took the train everywhere.

It wasn't so bad, actually. I quickly learned the process and would routinely purchase upgrades to a sleeper coach. I was traveling armed on this particular trip, so I had to identify myself. The conductors tracked where I was seated and felt a sense of comfort I was there in the event of an emergency. Trust me, though; all I was looking for was some rest and relaxation.

As we traveled back east, nearing Marceline, Missouri. I thought about how Walt Disney grew up there. In fact, the main street of Disneyland was modeled after his hometown's main street in the early 1900s. When Disney died, he'd had plans for a project in Marceline.

I felt a tap on my shoulder. "Could I see you in the back?" the conductor said.

I got up and followed him to a private spot.

"A lady is having a medical emergency," he said. "It might be a heart attack. Do you think you can help us out?"

"Are there any doctors or nurses on the train?" I asked.

"No. We'll put out an announcement. But in the meantime, can you come and help us?"

I ran with him to the coach just behind the restaurant car to find an older woman in her seat, reclined back, with her daughter in a panicked state, hovering over her. The woman was grabbing her chest and gasping for air. "Heart… pain…" was all she could say.

I turned to her daughter. "Is she on any medication?"

"Oh, yes! I forgot."

She grabbed an antique metal pill box and handed it to me. It was nitroglycerin tablets.

I checked the woman's vital signs. She looked terrible, now almost unconscious.

Tilting her chair back, I instructed the daughter to hold her head down and lift her tongue. I stuck a nitroglycerin pill under her tongue. It would absorb into her system faster there; these were the same instructions given to my father by his doctor in the event he'd ever suffered a heart attack. He had the same pills.

Five minutes later, as the train screeched to a halt at Marceline, her vitals came up. Before the EMTs came on board, she regained full consciousness.

"What did you give her?" an EMT asked me.

"A nitroglycerin pill," I replied.

"You realize you saved her life?" he said.

As I walked back to my seat, the passengers clapped. The conductor told me there was a sleeper open. He helped me move to it.

As I settled in, he said, "Anything you want, it's on the house. Just let me know."

"Thanks," I said. "But all I want right now is sleep."

"I can make that happen." He turned out the light and started closing the door. "You know," he whispered, "you're a good cop."

"Yeah," I said to the odd comment. "I'm just trying to survive like the next guy."

"You are. But it was at that moment I realized, in this profession, your watch never ends." Then, he closed the door.

I never heard anything about the woman after that. For me, it was "do your job and move on." No awards or congratulations needed. For the first time, I really knew the gravity of my new profession.

I had the Watch.

***

I finally reached home and my father. He was in bad shape, his heart failing. He still had his Coca-Cola franchise business, but there was no way he could run it.

Before I arrived, he had hired a few workers to run the two trucks and manage his affairs. After ensuring he was as good as possible, I checked on them to ensure everything was running smoothly. It was.

After a few days with my father, I realized he needed more attention than I had anticipated. I'd have no choice but to leave the Border Patrol to care for my father and the family business. I just couldn't go back with the degraded physical condition he was in.

So, with a heavy heart, I called my boss and gave him the bad news. He understood.

I hired a company to pack up my stuff and ship it back. And that was that, at least for now.

The first order of business was to find some income. My father didn't want me to live the same life he did; he wanted more for me, so I helped monitor the business while he recovered and kept a close eye on him. It was time to get creative; shifting gears from just being an active law enforcement officer was hard. So, I decided to fan out. I applied for anything close to home that was remotely related to law enforcement. In no time, I picked up work as an armored car supervisor.

It was an easy job if you set up everything correctly. I hired the right people. Did the background checks. Trained them in the proper procedures. Then, I stepped back and let them work. Most of them were retired Cops who wanted to stay in the game.

Because I needed more money than what it paid, I began serving the "process." Whenever a lawsuit is filed, paperwork—called process—must be served on the party in question. They need notice of the lawsuit.

Not sure why, but I was given the hard ones to serve. These were folks who ducked the servers or didn't answer the door. It paid more money, though, and that, in turn, paid the bills.

I used my imagination and dressed up as a pizza delivery person. I would approach the target's house and ring the doorbell. When they came to the door and looked out the peephole, I'd shout, "Pizza delivery!"

The individual would shout back, "I didn't order a pizza."

I'd say, "Well, it's paid for, and I already have this address listed as the person who paid for it. So, if someone messed up, you're getting a free pizza. It's hot and ready to eat."

Greed is a funny thing. Getting something for nothing is everyone's dream. So, I used it to my advantage.

Eventually, the target would open the door and say, "What type of pizza is it?"

"I don't know," I'd reply with an innocent expression on my face. "Let's look inside."

We would lift the lid together and find the paperwork sitting in the box. This led to puzzlement, anger, and then the ceremonial tossing of the paperwork at me.

I was sure not to put any real pizza in the box, or that would've also landed on me.

"You've been served," I'd tell them. "The judge will grant the plaintiff a default judgment if you fail to file an answer on time."

From down the road, I'd watch. After a few minutes, they would come outside and grab the paperwork. There was no way they wanted to default.

The other job I took was sweeping parking lots. That was related to law enforcement because police officers often perform sweeps for evidence or suspects. Sometimes, a police chief promises to sweep out the crime in a particular area.

I worked part-time Thursday and Friday after midnight with a heavy vacuum strapped to my back and the hose on my right hand. It was a tough job, especially during colder nights. I had to clean parking lots around bars where drunk patrons had vomited, defecated, and urinated. I sucked up everything, usually finishing at eight in the morning—just in time to start my armored car job.

Five nights a week, I'd lay my head on the pillow and think about my New York Military Academy days. They had a big sign at the entrance: "Through these portals, brave and gallant men shall pass. You shall pass through this life only but once. Do whatever good you can upon mankind during the time you're here on earth."

Was I fulfilling that proverb, that direction we were all given to go forth and do good?

Hardly.

The military academy wanted each graduate to become a flaming superstar. At that moment, I was more of a smoldering ember. I looked after my father and the business every moment, but I needed a break.

I continued applying again for any law enforcement job I could find. Despite a few nibbles, I spent the rest of 1993 working those three jobs. Finally, I got a bite, a hit. It was the New York State Department of Motor Vehicles.

My interview was with the chief investigator Frank Peterson. He was a former police lieutenant from New York. I felt confident I could wow him with my abilities from the patrol.

I found 80 Center Street in lower Manhattan, only a few steps from the Manhattan DA's Office where John Kennedy, Jr. worked. I walked inside, and it was as if the building had always stayed the same from when it had been built forty years earlier. Everything— the lights and décor—was from the fifties.

I pushed the elevator button and waited. With much creaking and moaning, the elevator descended, its doors parting.

"What floor, please?"

The operator was seated on a stool just inside the elevator. I knew from past experience that he was on a union contract elevator operator guarding the panel. He was the only one who could press a button. He was probably the last of the city's union elevator operators' holdouts.

"DMV Metro Frauds office," I said.

He frowned as he pressed a button. A minute later, I stood in an ancient hallway. Before I went in, I hit the men's room. I needed to check my look—my hair, tie, and suit—and ensure it was all in place before I stood before the boss.

As I passed the inspection, I smiled at the black-and-white checkered tile with the foot-controlled flushers. This restroom had to be older than the building—maybe the 1930s, if that was possible. Even the flush handles were located on the floor in the form of foot pedals, not a bad idea, really. Nonetheless, it was well cared for and very clean.

I left the bathroom and walked down to the Metro Frauds Office. A receptionist told me to have a seat.

It took ten minutes, but eventually, the chief investigator came out to get me. We walked to his office across old, creaking wooden floorboards. They creaked when you walked on them, and I swear I could see straight through to the floor below.

He instructed me to sit down in front of his desk. As I did, I noticed his desk was stacked high with mountains of documents and files. Completely cluttered and disorganized.

In the center of his desk rested an old Volkswagen hub cap. Occasionally, he tapped the long ash tube from his cigarette into the center.

What am I getting myself into? I thought.

I coughed a few times into the fog, hoping to find some un-poisoned air.

He put out his cigarette only to "lite" another one. A chain smoker, taking a deep drag, he coughed, pounded his chest three times, and cleared his throat. Then, he picked up my resume and began reviewing it—probably for the first time.

With nothing to do, while he looked over my resume, I studied my potential boss. It was winter in New York, but he was wearing a thin Members Only Jacket—the kind you get for free when you purchase a ten-ounce bottle of cologne. Underneath the jacket was

59

an old Fred Flintstone-style short sleeve pullover bowling shirt. Polyester pants pocked with cigarette burns led down to big black shoes that supported his 280-pound frame. When he coughed and pounded his chest again, I reanalyzed the situation.

First, he might not survive this interview. I was pretty sure that if you went on a job interview and the person interviewing you died, you wouldn't get hired. That had to be a rule somewhere.

Next, I considered that if he did survive and I got hired, he might die soon. That would move everyone up a notch. And given that the others had been breathing that secondhand smoke for years, they might not last very long either.

But then I considered the damage to my lungs. If I worked for this guy, my life expectancy would go down. With so many factors to weigh, it was going to be a tough call.

Chief Investigator Peterson set down my resume and began explaining the agency's mission. Suddenly, the door to his office flew open.

"I'm going to lunch," the senior investigator said. "You want me to bring you back something?"

Peterson reached into his pocket, pulling out two single dollar bills and handing them to the man.

"Wonton. Two bucks", he exclaimed.

The senior investigator nodded and left. Obviously, Peterson was very thrifty when it came to words and to lunch.

We resumed the interview. I told him about my past experience and current jobs. He was very interested in my ability to speak Spanish. When we reached the end of the interview session, he said, "Stay close to the phone."

I figured this was code for, "You got the job, but I don't have the authority to offer it to you. So, wait until human resources officially contacts you."

Of course, there was no way I was waiting by the phone. I had three separate jobs I was working.

Chapter 5

New York City Metro Frauds

After a long day of supervising men carrying bags of cash to and from stores and banks, I came home to a message on my answering machine.

"Tony Losito, this is Francine with human resources at the New York State Department of Motor Vehicles. The department would like to extend the position as an investigator to you. Please call and let me know if you are interested. Thank you."

Just like that, I was hired. No more parking lots filled with vomit or pizza delivery. I was back.

Like all law enforcement agencies, there was training to go through. The DMV put me through rigorous training that mostly covered document examination and auto theft. With memories of toting that heavy vacuum cleaner at two in the morning, I sucked up the information. Really, I got good at spotting fraudulent licenses and stolen cars.

Right out of training, I was assigned a case to investigate fraud in lower Manhattan. Complaints had been pouring in about drivers with fake licenses. These drivers were illegally parking, causing wrecks, hitting vehicles, and leaving the scene. It was a mess.

Lower Manhattan was a tight area. The streets had been laid out centuries earlier when horse-and-buggy carts delivered goods. Now, a large box truck going east and a UPS truck heading west on the same street made for all sorts of problems.

To bring some order to the area, the city stepped in and imposed strict rules regarding parking, direction of travel, and size of vehicles. Most of these rules were related to the time of day.

To operate transportation trucks, a driver needed a higher class of driver's license. This meant hours of class time, field training, and more time. And this translated into money.

Drivers with transportation licenses made more money. Yet delivery services didn't want to pay a lot. To solve the problem, the companies hired Chinese immigrants to drive. These immigrants couldn't speak English, and the street signs were in English. Somehow, though, these drivers obtained fraudulent paperwork. With a fake license in hand, a Chinese driver hit the road and, unfortunately, was not adequately prepared or a legal driver.

Because the department was understaffed, a rookie—me—was picked to help contribute to solving the caper. That pretty much tells you the priority level of this case.

The first thing any good investigator does is get the lay of the land. I spent a week in the license section, learning all the ins and outs of obtaining a license. By talking to the folks on the front lines, I had a good idea of how everything worked.

The next task involved poring over the complaints from citizens. After looking at the files, it appeared their licenses were legitimate. Somehow, these drivers were obtaining licenses when they had no ability to read and write English. It was a conundrum.

I went back to the front-line folks and asked more questions. Then, I hung out in an undercover capacity in the long lines, observing and studying the customers for any clues.

After days of this, I spotted one guy taking the test on repeated days. Because the place was so busy, I couldn't see everything he did. And I didn't speak Mandarin. I needed a translator with me so I could learn what was happening.

One day, while I was taking a break outside the building, eating a Chinese puff pastry. Trust me, if you've never had one, these creations were delicious. Chinatown in lower Manhattan was an amazing part of New York City, a treasure of a place. Great food and swelling with Chinese tradition. It was at this time; I realized a Chinese woman operated a stand-up booth against the building a block from where I worked. She sold these delicious puff pastries every morning until she ran out, usually around noon. I walked over and talked to her.

"Do you speak Mandarin?"

"Yes," she replied. "Do you buy pastry?"

The quicker she sold out, the quicker she could go to her next four jobs.

"Maybe," I said. "How would you like to help me out?"

"What I have to do?"

"Stand in line with me at the license section and pick up what's being said."

"How much it pay?" she asked.

"I'll buy plenty of pastries from you."

"How many?"

"Enough to help you get done faster."

She looked around the sidewalk. "You buy these. I go."

She had four dozen left. I reached into my pocket, pulled out one hundred dollars, and bought them all. That's another part of being in law enforcement you don't see on TV. There's so much stuff you need to help an investigation that isn't funded by wherever you work.

I took her to the license section. The line snaked out the door halfway around the block. We spent about an hour there. That's all she needed to help me gather key information on the case.

"Him," she said, pointing to the guy taking all the tests. "He take test for driver. Driver take picture. Stamp his fingers."

After processing this, I realized that when the test-taker passed the exam, he brought in his client to have his photo taken and fingerprints inked. It was a clever system. Test substitutions.

I worked for about the next two months on the case, feeding information to my supervisor. The agency ultimately arrested several people. Snakeheads, and illegal immigrant smugglers, were the catalyst behind most of the operation.

My case gave the higher-ups something to show the victims. It also moved me up the food chain. No pun intended to the puff pastries. However, a few months later, the snakeheads had solved the problem and were right back at it. That's another fact of law enforcement. Build a nice sandcastle, only to have it washed away the next day. Then, build it again.

Their needs and their system were much larger than any of us.

***

I worked on some other cases for a few months before being assigned back to the main office, the one where I first interviewed. Walking past the receptionist and inhaling that smoke, I wondered how long I could take it. Because clearly, Chief Investigator Peterson had no problems with it.

I went to see the human chimney. Peterson sent me to my new boss, three offices over. Tapping lightly on the door, I found a woman standing over her desk, twirling handcuffs while talking on the phone. Her shoulder-length red hair was mostly tamed, with just a touch of wildness. She looked to be all woman yet a cop you didn't want to cross. I was intrigued.

"Sit there," she whispered, covering the mouthpiece.

I sat down in an ancient office chair, its rollers barely moving. Where the hell was the budget for this organization, it was obvious they were last on the list of funding.

"Take one of those desks," she whispered. "Just pick one."

I looked around the office and saw four desks. Two of them were occupied. I decided to take the one farthest from the door to minimize the secondhand smoke drifting in. Besides, it was closest to the window.

The chair at my desk was at least twenty years older than the one at her desk.

Unbuttoning my jacket, I smoothed out my slacks before sitting down. This was my best suit. I spent good money on it. In reality, it was my only suit at the time. Because I had been doing print modeling on the side before the Patrol, I knew you only got one chance to make a good first impression. Getting a new boss was one of those occasions.

I sat there for several minutes, waiting for her to get off the phone and assign me some cases. But before she could, two senior investigators walked in.

A muscle-bound investigator loomed over me. "Yo, homeboy, you're in my seat."

"My name is Tony," I said meekly. "I was just assigned here, and she (nodding towards her) told me to take a desk."

"I don't give a crap what your name is, hotshot. That's my desk."

"But I don't have anywhere to sit."

He moved closer.

"That's not my problem. Now, I'm going to grab a cup of coffee. When I come back, if you're still in that chair, we're going to have a problem. And it might get solved with a hot cup of coffee."

I sat there contemplating this situation. I had dealt with bullies all my life. They didn't scare me. Most of them were just afraid of something.

I thought of what the consequences would be if we got into a physical confrontation. Would I get suspended? Fired?

Thoughts of cleaning up poop and vomit in parking lots brought me back to sanity.

I put my hands on the desk and stood up. As I did, a loose spring in the chair caught my pants and ripped them wide open.

It was bad. Worse than bad. I mean really bad.

My boss motioned me over as she finished the conversation. Seeing the back of my ass exposed, I wrapped my suit jacket around my waist, tying the arms together like you did back in high school.

"What's your problem?" she asked, looking at my high school getup.

"I ripped my pants sitting in that chair."

She frowned. "We don't have any money for chairs or desks. You're supposed to put a magazine down before you sit on it, and I'm not paying for your pants either."

"Thanks for the advice. I'll remember that."

"Now, stop screwing around; the boss wants to see you," she said.

"Oh, man. You've got to be kidding me."

"Nope."

I went to see Peterson, using my knife to cut through the smoke. I found him sitting there, studying two one-dollar bills. Obviously, lunchtime was looming. Either that, or he had some type of fraud case he was about to give me, maybe counterfeit bills. Hopefully, I'd get to work with the Secret Service or some agency that had a decent budget.

"Wonton," he said, thrusting the money at me. "Two bucks."

Really? I thought.

I took his money, unable to take my eyes off the three-inch ash tube hanging from his cigarette and hoovering over the automobile hub cap on his desk that doubled as an ashtray.

"Go!" he yelled when I didn't move.

Unable to solve this mystery, I went back to my new supervisor and asked her to help me decode his order of "Wonton, two bucks!"

What was this cryptic mission, I thought.

She said, "Go over to Chinatown, 66 Bleaker Street. Walk down to the basement and get him two bucks' worth of wonton soup. Make sure the lid is on tight before you leave."

"But my pants are ripped," I pleaded with her.

"And I'm on my period. But I didn't let that stop me from coming into work. Toughen up, Donnie."

"Tony," I said quietly.

"Whatever."

I ran the errand and came back. The whole time thinking, this was like a job out of the twilight zone.

After enduring stares from the elevator operator again, I handed Peterson his order. Then, I watched as he popped off the lid and sipped the soup until it was all gone. No spoon, straight from the tall plastic container.

Another lit cigarette to replace the one that had just gone out a microsecond earlier, a few coughs, three good fists to the chest, and he was good as new.

I turned to leave, but he stopped me.

"Meet your new partner," he said.

I turned around, waving my hands through the fog. Barely visible was a man in his late twenties, wearing a decent suit and strapped with a clean Jackson Browne haircut.

"This is Wild Bill," Peterson said. Your new partner.

"Wild Bill, this is Donnie."

"Ahh, Tony sir," I said, moving closer to shake his hand. That's when I noticed his arm jerk in different directions.

Studying him for a few seconds, I watched his face and neck twitch. In the few seconds I observed him, I was sure he was Rodney Dangerfield's son.

"Hi-ho-hey," Wild Bill said.

"What's up with all this?" I asked, referring to his twitching. The last thing I needed was being cornered by some thug and having Wild Bill come to my rescue. I could see his twitching hand pulling out a pistol and aiming it at both the bad guys and me. I didn't like those odds.

"Not a problem, just a little hyperactive. I didn't take my medicine today."

"Oh," I said.

"Hi-ho-hey," he blurted out.

"Do you have Tourette's?" I asked.

"No, but I have some Sucrets."

At some point, my mind switched off as my body floated above the ceiling tiles. Surely this was some hidden camera show. No way this was real.

Peterson brought me back to earth. "He lives four hours away in Connecticut."

I furrowed my brow. "So?" "What's that to me?"

Peterson coughed. "He needs a place local to stay, just until he gets settled."

"Oh, no!"

"I've been taking care of my brother, my sister, and my dad. I need some me time."

"But I have no place to live. Take a look at these baby blues." Wild Bill stared at me, his head jerking every few seconds. "You don't want me to sleep on the street, do ya."

"Bill, how can you have no place to live?" I asked.

"Wild Bill!" he said, not twitching for the first time. "You heard him."

"Okay. Wild Bill."

"I haven't got a paycheck yet. I just need a few weeks to get on my feet."

I played my last card. "But I live at Dobbs Ferry, right across from a bar. The apartment is crappy. It's over a Chinese restaurant. The place routinely smells of fried egg rolls and number three with rice. Good in one sense because I love Chinese food, bad in another because I can't eat it every night."

The one window I have opens up to a brick wall. It's like the scene from Woody Allen's movie Take the Money and Run."

"Sounds perfect," he said. "I love Chinese food. It's so good for you."

"Now that that's settled," Peterson said, "here's your first case. Go crack it open."

He handed us a file. Wild Bill grabbed it, but I snatched it out of his hand. "I'll take that. With your shaking and jerking, these papers will be all over the place."

He gave up easily, which made me wonder what he'd do when the thug had me on the ground and was about to shoot me in the head.

***

Wild Bill and I worked on all types of cases. Most consisted of fake document capers. It was cheaper to create a fake title than to pay the fees and taxes. And the penalties for getting caught were usually minimal.

We eventually moved into organized crime, mainly auto theft rings. Before long, I became trained as an auto theft investigator.

Wild Bill continued living with me, paying some of the rent and refusing to find his own place. I got used to it, especially when I began dating. Staying with a new girlfriend gave Wild Bill the entire place to himself.

One day, he came home and announced, "Your hair is thinning out."

"Yes, Bill, I'm aware; I don't need you to remind me."

"I already knew that."

I've been doing runway and print work for the past few years. Each time I sat in the dressing room, the mirrors displayed my receding peak and a growing bald spot in the back. When I did print work, they shot the right angles, avoiding the baldness. They made me look like Wild Bill, with ten square feet of hair on my head. But I knew the cold, hard truth: I was thinning badly.

I thanked Wild Bill for his astute observation. Then, I ground my teeth to the nubs as I went to see Tim, my friend from high school.

"Here," he said, tossing me a can. "Do what they do in Hollywood. Spray this on your bald spot."

I tried it at Tim's apartment. The black spackle worked like a charm. But it was a complete mess. If I touched it, I came back with a handful of black powder. It was hard to get off.

"Thanks so much," I said to Tim, clutching the can like a baby. "My balding days are over."

Or so I thought.

***

I've been using a black spray for two weeks. So far, no one has picked up on it.

At night, I didn't want my new girlfriend—to find out I had it on. I learned fast that it stained pillowcases. To solve this problem, I slept all night with an arm underneath my head. It hurt and was awkward, but at least it hid my secret.

One day, I walked into the office and learned Peterson had been promoted. In his place was Joseph Dove. He had just retired as a sergeant from the NYPD after twenty-five hard years. He was another chain smoker in the office too. Gesh, What were the odds?

He had this spooky mustard-gas stare, the kind that looked straight through you.

"Gesh, I thought, this is going to be tough to deal with."

I sat in his office when he got up from his chair. "How does my ass look in these pants?" he said.

"You can't ask me that," I said, looking away. "What's wrong with you?"

He sat back down. I went for broke.

"And why do you stare at the wall like a zombie?"

"You try sitting at the end of the runway at JFK for a year and a half on a horrible patrol assignment, listening to jet engines behind those blast shields because you got punished when you screwed up on a case. That was my penance and my last post. Over time, your brain turns to mush."

I nodded, staring at the ground. There wasn't much I could say.

"Get in the room with Nicole," he said. "She's doing a refresher on handcuffing techniques."

"Handcuff techniques?" I said, protesting.

"Yeah. Some cop was beaten up when his collar (an arrested suspect) slipped the cuffs and went all crazy on him. The department sent out a memo."

"Oh, man," I said. "What a waste of time."

"Shut the heck up and get in the room."

I went to the training room and found Nicole there.

She had an array of restraints and handcuffs spread out on the table. The other investigators stood around, waiting for something to happen. After Dove and I arrived, she began the refresher course.

"Tony," she said, "get down on the ground. You're going to be our first subject. We're going to do some compliant handcuffing."

This was absolutely the last thing I wanted anyone to do to me. Not only had I ripped my best suit working here but touching any part of my head would blow my black spray secret. I decided to stay where I was.

"Tony, get on the ground."

I didn't move.

The stares from the other guys were piercing. They didn't want to be here any longer than I did. My hesitation was wasting everyone's time.

She commanded me four times to get on the ground. Each time, I ignored her.

Finally, my boss yelled, "Get down on the ground!"

I reluctantly dropped to my knees, raising my hands so she didn't have to touch my hair.

"I'm going to demonstrate how to do compliant handcuffing of a subject that's on the ground."

Before I could react, she had inserted her left arm between my arms, shoving the inside of her hand under my nose. This is a standard armbar technique. A split second later, she grabbed the back of my hair.

Grabbing a big clump of spray on hair. Completely shocked, she screamed.

"What the hell?" with her thick Bronx accent ringing in my ears.

I spun my head around. My worst fears had come true. Her hand was covered in black paste.

Nicole raised her hand up as if from a movie scene where the bad guy just accidentally dipped his hand in acid.

Staring at her hand held high for the whole room to see, she shouted, "What the hell is this!" She then rubbed the clean hand over the infected one, and they both went dark.

Before I could say anything, she bolted out of the room.

With mouths hanging open, everyone watched as I then ran out of the room, too, and went to the bathroom with my hair repair kit. Once there, I spoofed up my hair, straightened my clothes, and went back to work.

My hope was that they would all forget what they'd seen and not say a word. But those hopes were quickly dashed.

"What in God's name is going on with you?" Nicole asked.

"Relax," I replied. "I'm dealing with a crisis."

"Which is?"

"I'm a guy losing my hair crisis."

When everyone started laughing, I figured something was up.

It turned out she had arranged the whole charade because they had already been tipped off by none other than you know who? Yip, Wild Bill.

Even though I endured endless jokes, at least I could stop sleeping with my arm underneath my head. That was something to be thankful for on this rodeo ride my career was taking.

Chapter 6

New York Terrorism
Trials Operations Command

I n 1986, before I started losing my hair, I attended the John Casablanca School for Modeling. I had always wanted to be an actor. It has been my dream since I could remember.

When I was younger, while at New York Military Academy, I was selected to be part of several commercials filmed at the school: Lipton Soup, Planers Peanuts, and Time Magazine. This was a lot of fun, so I figured the best way to break into the career was to learn how to be in front of a camera.

The school taught me how to be in front of the lens. It also enabled me to assemble my first photo portfolio. The whole deal had set me back $1,000, which was a lot of cash then. But I was still working for Pepsi and making a good living.

Casablanca used my portfolio to show casting directors and producers. At the time, I was much younger, and the demand for my services was greater.

I landed my first gig with Avon. I appeared in their home catalog for various products. With that under my belt, I was able to hire an agent. She was dubbed the "Lysol Queen" because she had appeared in commercials for the household cleaner in the seventies and eighties. My new agent helped me land a few gigs like print work and runway jobs. However, as soon as my media career started, it began to slow down when I pursued a career in law enforcement.

Now that I was back home again in New York, I decided to get back into acting and modeling. I picked up a few side gigs. The extra income had been a nice supplement to the low government pay. But I came to the realization that my modeling and acting days (in front of the camera, that is) were over. With a need to make some extra money, I sat down and studied my budget.

The words of Mr. Sanchez continued to echo in my brain. "Seek the highest three consecutive years of pay."

Because I was employed by the state of New York, I wasn't in the federal retirement program. With the wacky world of DMV assaulting me each day, I needed to look for something with the feds and get back into the game where I started.

In February 1993, about a year before I came to the DMV, the World Trade Center was bombed. Six people were killed. Over one thousand were injured. It was a terrible act.

The perpetrators were eventually captured, and trials were scheduled. One of them—Sheikh Omar Abdel-Rahman—was set to start on January 30, 1995. The U.S. Federal Protective Service Police needed more bodies for this trial. They put out the word that they needed Police Officers.

I sat in the DMV each day, staring at the security across the street where the trials occurred. So, it prompted me to check out the Federal Protective Service.

After reading up on them, I learned they were responsible for protecting federal employees, buildings, and property. The low end of the job was basic security. On the upper end was promotion to Special Agent. It sounded interesting to me.

I turned in an application to be a Federal Protective Service Police Officer and was immediately hired. After saying goodbye to the cast of characters at the DMV, I was quickly trained and deployed.

The huge concern was with the World Trade Center. The terrorists had tried and failed to take it down.

We knew they probably wanted a second crack at it. As part of the strategy to combat this, the Federal Protective Service placed me and other uniformed Police Officers on various high-visibility security posts. They also sent me to patrol the World Trade Center. They already had plenty of guys patrolling the courthouse where the trial was underway. This was the next priority.

Because they wanted a lower profile, I would often dress down. I still had a bulletproof vest with a standard windbreaker with a badge and Police written on the back. Still, I was in blue jeans instead of a standard police uniform. As for vehicles, they put me in the law enforcement unmarked Chevy Caprice.

I began patrolling the Plaza, specifically the U.S. Customs House, (6 World Trade Center), and 7 World Trade Center. Both locations housed federal employees at the time. Immediately, I drew the attention of the Port Authority Police. An officer stopped my patrol car and told me to report it to the Captain. As I parked the Caprice, I wondered what I had done that their Captain had summoned me.

The Port of Authority is a state-run agency, a combination of New York and New Jersey.

Because I worked for the feds, they had no jurisdiction over our agency. Still, I was in New York. Once you learn how things work, you quickly understand that territory is very important to all kinds of folks. The Port Authority was responsible for protecting aspects of the World Trade Center. Still, we had the responsibility to protect the federal property within the boundaries of the Trade Center.

That meant I had stepped on part of their turf without their permission. Now, I had to go meet the Captain and maybe "kiss his ring" so I could receive his blessing to continue my work. Trust me, it's just how things work in New York.

Two uniformed officers escorted me to the lower level of the World Trade Center, about three levels below the surface. All I could think of was the opening scene of the TV Show Get Smart. There he was, sitting in a dimly lit office, poring over a map.

"What's your name?" he asked curtly, not looking up from his desk or bothering to shake my hand.

"Tony Losito," I replied.

He finally looked up. "Tony. That's a good Italian name. Right?"

"Yes, sir, it is."

"Italians. I love the Italians because they get it. Do you get it, Tony?"

"Get what, sir?"

"That you're on our turf without my permission. Why is that Tony?"
"Why didn't you announce?"

"Because we share jurisdiction here, and I have been directed by my supervisor to patrol 6 & 7 World Trade Center." That was what I wanted to say. Instead, the diverter valve in my brain sent out this response, "Captain, you've got a fantastic department here! I can't tell you how much I appreciate the Port Authority Police. I know I can't add anything to the excellent job you do here. But I'm here just to complement the operation. I'm one extra body, a low-level grunt who promises not to get in the way of the fine work you're doing."

He frowned and looked away in disgust. After a few moments of wasting my time simply because he could, he dismissed me with a wave. In case I decided to steal something, two officers escorted me out.

On the way back to my patrol car, I thought about all this. I knew from my time with the DMV that the New York Police Department had a lot of cops who'd left for the Port Authority. And the reverse was true with cops leaving the Port Authority to work for the NYPD. Turf was very important to them both.

I had been told that before any law enforcement officer went into a territory controlled by the NYPD, they needed to find an officer with rank to make the introduction to the local supervisor or detective. It's like with organized crime. You don't talk to a boss without an introduction from someone he trusts.

My shift continued uninterrupted the rest of the day. Occasionally, I waved at a Port Authority officer patrolling beside me. I always had a big smile on my face, so they knew how happy I was working next to—or with—them.

The next morning, I told my supervisor about what had happened. He was very pleased I had gone and met the Captain. He had too much going on to drive over there and make friends. "Besides," he said, "when you need help with a suspect, you want to make sure they'll be there to help you. If not, we might be wearing a black armband in remembrance of Officer Losito."

He was right on. As petty and time-wasting as it was, kissing the local ring was better than having no one respond to an "officer needs assistance" call. It had happened before. I was quickly learning the rules of the game.

After I'd patrolled for a few weeks, my boss pulled me off the detail to provide more security around the courthouse. Our mission was called the New York Terrorism Trials Operation Command or loosely abbreviated as NYTTOC.

At first, the command put me on uniformed patrol. Then they switched me to undercover work, dressing me up as a homeless person. I was ordered to watch key individuals in the area; the goal was to protect the safety of the trails.

At the time, we believed these specific individuals that were loitering around the courthouse and lower Manhattan area to conduct surveillance and potentially exchange information. We could have approached them, but it was easier just to keep an eye on their activities. Once you drive your opponent underground, you create more work by having to find him again.

I routinely found suspicious packages around the U.S. Bankruptcy building and 26 Federal Plaza, which I believed to be tests or diversions at the time. I quickly passed everything up the chain of command for the appropriate review and decision.

I soon learned I had more experience than most patrol officers I worked with. Even though some officers had extensive college backgrounds, they didn't have street experience. On the other hand, my time in Border Patrol, the Air Force, and the DMV had me well-suited for the undercover work. I wasn't there to fight the seven major crimes: rape, robbery, burglary, murder, aggravated assault, simple assault, and grand theft auto. I was there to protect the sanctity of the trial. If we all did our jobs right, nothing would happen.

Several months into my undercover work on the trial, I was pulled back to work uniform patrol. Our office began to experience a shortage of patrol officers at that time. Many officers were using the role as a steppingstone to become special agents or move up the food chain in law enforcement. The long 12-hour shifts took their toll on officers, and they soon sought a nice cozy office environment.

Command placed me in the lobby of 26 Federal Plaza in Lower Manhattan. 26 Federal Plaza is the main federal building in Lower Manhattan. The building is so large and busy that it has its own zip code, 10278. Between 26 Federal Plaza and the other federal facilities surrounding it, there are reputed to be more federal employees concentrated in that area alone than in any other area outside of Washington, D.C.

Right across the street from 26 Federal Plaza is 290 Broadway, a federal building, and 40 Foley Square, the U.S. Courthouse. Nearby is 400 Cadman Plaza and the older U.S. Courthouse. Finally, there's the Metropolitan Detention Center. That packs a ton of federal folks all together.

My job was to serve as a uniformed police officer, a visible security, and police presence in the area to support the federal community. On this day, I was inside 26 Federal Plaza, observing visitors who might enter the building. I was also assigned the collateral detail of protecting the childcare center. For me, it was just another routine day.

I stood there watching and observing, acting as a visible deterrent and ambassador to those frequenting the building. Strategically placing uniformed cops around the facility tends to deter criminal conduct. That's why not much happens when an officer is standing there.

Back then, we didn't have television monitors posted for people to watch the news. We had walkie-talkies set to police frequencies. That's how we got most of our news.

From where I was posted, I could see the FBI office's main doors in the lobby. A compartmented area separates from the rest of the main lobby, which stood out by two unique sets of secured glass doors and a nice sign and decal that read FBI. Its glass doors continually swung open as employees walked in and out of the office all day. Inside, the FBI screened everyone that came and went. Nothing got in or out without their permission.

As I stood there maintaining my post, I noticed the glass doors suddenly and with force swinging open so hard that they hit the wall, making a loud noise. Then, a wave of FBI agents came crashing out. One agent ran up to me and said, "Officer! Officer!

We just lost a building in Oklahoma City. Secure this location immediately!"

"Lost a building?" I said, confused.

"Yes! They just took down the Murrah Federal Building in Oklahoma City. We haven't figured out what's happening yet, but someone just blew it up no more than ten minutes ago."

I grabbed my walkie-talkie and relayed the information up the chain of command and to our command center. They had already heard something, and my FBI information confirmed it.

I immediately rushed over to the childcare center. I marshaled all the workers and children—infants, toddlers, and kids of all ages— to a secure location. Thankfully, we had practiced the drill before, so I knew what to do.

Other patrol officers came to the building to help. We didn't force everyone to immediately leave or "dump" the building as we used to call it. Still, tenants and visitors could stay and finish business as we didn't want to instill shock and fear, causing everyone to panic.

During our morning briefings, we were constantly told about the chance for multiple attacks to occur simultaneously worldwide. Like we'd later see in Mumbai. The fact that Oklahoma City was the site of this attack didn't make us rest any easier. We could only think, would our building be next?

Thankfully, it wasn't.

At the end of the day, the relieved parents came to the secure location where we took the kids and retrieved their children. They were thankful beyond measure. Once the building was empty, anti-terrorism officers arrived. We searched the entire building, inspecting every nook and cranny. Another group combed the exterior. It was only later into the evening that night when we received the all-clear. It took a long time to literally secure a building that size.

The next morning, we let people back into the facility, but only with much more enhanced screening measures. Everything was super tight for a while.

We learned soon after the bombing that the perpetrator, Timothy McVeigh, was in custody. He had parked a truck full of explosives in front of the Alfred P. Murrah Federal Building in downtown Oklahoma City. He ignited several drums filled with a mixture of agricultural fertilizer, diesel fuel, and other chemicals, lit the fuse, and drove off. As he sped away from the crime, an observant Oklahoma State Trooper spotted a vehicle with a missing license plate. He just happened to be conducting vehicle and traffic stops— "V & Ts," or vehicle and traffic stops, as we call it in the police jargon.

When the Trooper questioned McVeigh about it, he noticed a bulge in his coat. McVeigh admitted he had a firearm and produced a permit. Unfortunately, the permit was not valid in Oklahoma. Because of this, the Trooper arrested McVeigh and placed him in custody, and then the local jail.

And there he was three days later when agents connected him with the bombing. For the Trooper, he was simply doing his job. That's what police work is: everyone doing their job, no matter how small or trivial it may seem. It's up to management to put us in the right spots to make a difference. All we have to do is our jobs.

This particular State Trooper was recognized for his outstanding work, as he should be. The Federal Protective Service also recognized officers for doing their jobs well. I received an award from my agency for my work during the trial and that event. They called it a "fast track" award. It really raised my morale, and I very much appreciated being recognized for doing a good a great job.

Again, that's policing. All I did was observe activities and kick them upstairs. I had no idea what they did with the information, and I didn't need to know. I had a role and embraced it. I might be checking out packages left behind or guarding a building entrance. I always wanted to do more, but that would mean moving up.

Today, I inform all new officers that you may think you're just a tiny sparkplug in a big engine. But if you aren't doing your job, the engine might not work. You've got to show up each day, follow orders, and work hard. Stand the watch. Your work, as little as you may feel it is, saves lives and protects the innocent.

That was what the Oklahoma Trooper was doing just that the day he caught the world's biggest mass murderer on U.S. soil. He was assigned to an area and worked hard. The net his management had cast landed McVeigh. The Trooper was part of a big net and did his job. If he had been deficient, McVeigh might have continued and potentially blown-up other buildings and killed even more innocent people. Now, the Trooper is a hero, and McVeigh is where he is supposed to be.

That's policing at its core.

Chapter 7

Hurricane Marilyn Response, US Virgin Islands

I continued working on the trial throughout the spring and summer. However, in September of 1995, Hurricane Marilyn ripped through the Caribbean, devastating the U.S. Virgin Islands. FEMA was called into action.

Right after it hit, my boss called me into the office and handed me a list.

"Tony, I need you to pack these items along with two weeks of equipment and supplies and be ready for the transport tonight at midnight."

"Where am I going?" I asked, completely confused.

"To the Virgin Islands."

"Why?"

"To secure the federal buildings and establish law and order. Later, you'll protect the FEMA workers and their headquarters as they dispense aid throughout the islands."

He went on to tell me that the Caribbean was in our jurisdiction. He wanted me and a team of agents to get there fast. He had reports that the locals were looting, breaking into stores, and taking over the U.S. Attorney's office. Numerous prisoners had been released from jail and committed crimes everywhere around the island of Saint Thomas. It was mass pandemonium, he explained.

He also told me the governor of the islands had called the White House and said he was locked in his mansion, barricaded, and feared for his life. The governor claimed he was under siege and had just a few local police officers he still trusted, along with his two fiercely loyal Doberman Pinchers. He had released the dogs onto his property for protection. Even though there was a fence around his property, it wouldn't hold long.

"Get down here as fast as possible!" he told those he spoke to.

"This island is going crazy. It's under siege!"

"Listen up," my boss said.

"You and your team will be securing the U.S. Attorney's office on the island of St Thomas. The information we are receiving tells us that not only has it been hammered by the storm, but roving gangs are preventing the employees from getting to the office. They're taking over the island. I want you to first secure that building."

"Okay. Then what?"

"Then, you'll secure the docks so supplies can come through and then work on restoring order to the island."

I took notes and listened. He said we'd be flying into Puerto Rico and joining a local law enforcement team that was forming up. From there, we'd all fly on to St. Thomas.

The military had already sent the Air Force Combat Controllers to the island. They were special operation guys who routinely landed in jungles and created airstrips out of nothing.

"The airport had been overrun with bad guys," my boss said.

"They control it now. Hopefully, the military will maintain control by the time you land. If they don't, it'll be a hot landing. So be prepared."

"Will they be assisting in securing the island?" I asked.

"No, they'll stay at the airport and keep it secure. Your job is to protect the federal facilities, the government employees, and FEMA as they distribute food and water and render aid. You and Ralphie will be the team leaders."

I took a deep breath. I shook his hand and was at the door when he added, "Tony, armor up!"

He got that right. I planned on being as prepared as possible.

***

We worked to prepare for the night, and by very early the next morning, we landed in San Juan, Puerto Rico. The local team met us. All ten of us then walked over to a twin-engine puddle jumper. The second I saw it, the blood drained from my face.

Even though I had been in the Air Force, I still feared flying. I always felt a loss of control when I climbed onto the plane. My worry wasn't so much that it was my time to go. If that was the case, I was okay because I'd been saved. I knew where I was heading. My biggest worry was that it might be the pilot's time to go. I didn't want to end up in heaven decades early, trying to explain the mix-up. That's why I prefer train or vehicle travel. But I couldn't boat to the island; time was of the essence.

Yet you must pull on your big boy pants when you're in law enforcement. Sometimes, you have to suit up and kick down a door. Or chase a bad guy down a dark alley. Sure, we feel fear. Although I like to call it "concern." But we push through it and get the job done.

As a team leader, I had to be strong and not show any weakness or fear of flying; it just wasn't appropriate. It would undermine my authority once we hit the island. And this was a situation where I needed complete command and control.

Before we took off, the local team told us the airport had just been fully secured, and there was no question about who had control. That was a huge relief.

We loaded up our gear as the men climbed the stairs. On the tarmac, Ralphie, my partner, grabbed my arm. "Tony, I'm not getting on that friggin' plane. There's too much weight in men alone without the gear. Add in all the ammo, and we'll go down like a rock."

I pushed his logic to the back of my mind. "Come on. We'll be fine" I was lying to him; honestly, I felt exactly the same way.

"No, we won't," he said.

"Look at this plane. It's a piece of "shit." The fiberglass over the propeller already has a crack." He led me over to inspect it. Sure enough, there was a crack. Still, I had to maintain a semblance of control combined with ease. I was just as concerned but had to tell myself we would make the flight. Any less confidence in my own mind, and I would not have boarded the plane.

"Ralphie, people could be potentially dying over there. We need to stop the madness and get over there. Besides, the federal government would not have us take off in a plane that wasn't safe."

I switched to my calm voice.

"But if the plane does go down, we'll glide to the sea and make a smooth landing. Then we'll quietly exit the aircraft and swim to the island."

"Swim? Have you already started smoking that ganja they sell over there, Tony? You're crazy. No way we glide to a nice safe landing and walk away?"

My vocal tone wasn't working. As a last resort, I had to reach deep down and pull out some special B.S. Hopefully, that will work.

"Look, the feds have hired the best pilots around. Real professional stick jockeys. I'll bet one of them looks like Tom Cruise from Top Gun. They're not going to let this plane crash, Brother, besides if we go down, we go down together. It would be an honor to take my last flight with a Marine." (Ralphie had served honorably in the United States Marine Corps in his earlier days.)

That did the trick. Ralphie rubbed his jaw, closed his eyes, and eventually climbed the stairs ahead of me to take his seat.

As team leaders, we sat in the front, me on the side with the crack, and him right behind me. Just sitting there waiting for the pilots to show up, I turned around and saw Ralphie's knuckles turning white. His grip on the armrests was vicelike. I was going to tell him to relax when I noticed my knuckles were the same way. I tried breathing slowly to bring my heart rate down, but it didn't work. Honestly, I was concerned.

After ten minutes of me sweating bullets with Ralphie, the pilots exited the terminal. They started their long walk across the tarmac. As they came into focus, my heart sank even lower. Both pilots were very big guys around the waist, with each one carrying a bag of burritos. That increased the overall weight on the plane; hey, burritos can weigh a lot.

Apparently, they had been making so many trips they hadn't eaten a thing all day or in the last twenty minutes.

Because they approached from our side, I tried blocking the window so Ralphie couldn't see. But when they set foot on the stairs, the plane rocked itself over. That turned Ralphie's eyes into large white saucers.

"Tony. No way, Tony. No way. Those burritos must weigh a hundred pounds each."

I glanced at the pilots, who had taken up residence in the cockpit. They were pushing buttons with one hand and shoving back a burrito with the other. Sauce dripped everywhere, on their white shirts and the instrument panel. As the first officer wiped some sauce off the instruments, I distracted Ralphie. Strangely, trying to calm him suppressed my fear as well.

Barely.

Before they started the engines, the captain opened his small door and looked out. The engines whined as they got up to speed. After a minute of running, he gunned the engines to get us moving.

The plane rolled along the tarmac at a steady pace. This gave them time to eat burritos and drip more sauce. Occasionally, they pressed more buttons and looked out the doors. It was completely crazy.

When the plane was at the end of the runway, the captain gunned it hard, and we lurched forward. The entire time down the runway, he had the door open, staring at something on the ground. This was the old Isla Grande Airport in San Juan. The runway ended in the ocean. I could see the white caps on the waves as we approached the end. It was clear we were too heavy and would crash in the blue water. I gripped the armrest harder and prepared myself for a brief swim. Or a meeting with my maker.

Somehow, the captain lifted the plane up two to three feet as he crossed over the ocean. Then he closed the door as the engines sputtered to gain altitude.

Ralphie leaned over and whispered in a panicked voice, "I just know that crack is getting wider. Tony, we're never going to see our wives and family again; forget about the island?"

Family.

Well, that comment struck a raw nerve. My Dad and Mom. Italian and Irish. Gasoline and fire. What a pair they made.

My father had grown up on the Italian side of Fordham Road. On the opposite side were the Irish. Dad walked up and down Fordham Road, looking for a Sofia Loren, he told me when I was young. When he couldn't find one, he crossed over to the Irish section and found Mom. They quickly married and lived in Yonkers, New York. Mom was just eighteen when I was born.

From an early age, I always saw Mom walking around with a drink in her hand. While others carried thermoses filled with coffee, hers was stuffed with scotch.

The other problem with my parents was control. My father possessed none of it. Instead, he provided enforcement while Mom was the brains of the family. She made the decisions, and my father carried the luggage to wherever she pointed with a free hand that wasn't holding a scotch.

Unfortunately, my father didn't have the authority or the ability to get my mother to stop drinking. It continued out of control. And she got violent akin to the movie "Mommie Dearest."

I was sixteen. One morning, my mother said contemptuously, "You've got beady eyes. Every time I look at you, I see your father."

That was apparently it on her end. With that, she grabbed a fully loaded shotgun and put it to my head. Then, she cocked the trigger back and told me to get out of the house because I had refused to testify for her—and against my father—in divorce court.

"You're a traitor!" she screamed. "Get out of my house!"

The day before, she had made an appointment to take me to her attorney so he could massage my testimony and get me to say the right things to help my mother's argument. I refused to go.

"Your divorce is between you and him, not him and me," I said.

A month later, I had a date coming to pick me up in her car. She pulled into the driveway as my mom ran out of the house. By now, the attorneys had arranged for me to pick where I wanted to live when the divorce was final. No kid should ever be put in that position.

She yelled at me, "You'll go down with him and have nowhere to live. You'll be sorry."

When I ignored her, she tossed a scotch on the rocks at me. I watched as the glass shattered on the driveway, sending ice cubes sliding into the grass. Frustrated she had missed, Mom picked up an ax leaning against the porch, but the ax head fell off. Not to be deterred, she ran toward me with the handle.

Seeing this, my girlfriend backed up and left me stranded. My only move was to hop on my bike and ride to a neighbor's house to sleep. It was terrible and traumatic.

But the real drama happened a few months after all this when my father arrived to grab a few things out at the house before the divorce was final. My mother, who was sheltered in a prison of anger and bitterness, began ragging at my father. He turned the other cheek until she got violent. Then, he tried to talk to her rationally. That only escalated matters. His calmness was interpreted as demeaning by her.

As the conversation turned heated, my father clutched his chest and fell to the ground. My mother, in a drunken state, took the opportunity to jump on his chest.

She screamed, "Die! Die, you son of a bitch! Die!"

At the time, I was on the football team and tungsten steel strong. Just as my mother began punching him in the face and chest, I lifted her up and tossed her toward the wall. My mother's butt crashed through the sheetrock, leaving her in a seated position. She was stuck for a solid ten minutes. It was like in the movies when the bad guy is down for a few seconds, and the hero has just enough time to escape.

I called an ambulance, and they rushed my father to the hospital. He had suffered a heart attack and yet somehow survived, no thanks to her.

So, yeah. Family as I reflected.

"Tony, I can see the island," Ralphie said, jostling me back to reality. "I think we're gonna make it!"

I stared out the window at the sun that was well above the horizon. On the ground below us, everything was a complete disaster. Trees stripped clean. Planes flipped over like toys. Boats were beached everywhere. Debris and bodies floated back and forth in the surf. What a nightmare.

As we exited the plane, Ralphie approached the pilot and asked him why he'd had the door open on takeoff. The pilot picked at a piece of meat stuck between his teeth. "Because the plane was so heavy, we didn't know if we would get off the ground. We had to examine the separation between the ground and the plane."

Ralphie grabbed my arm. "I told you, Tony! I'm not ever flying with these guys again. I'll take a boat to get to the mainland. If I have to, I'll make a new life on this island. My family can come to visit."

I nodded because, truthfully, I didn't want to get back on a plane either; I was thinking the same thing. I figured it was best to let some time go by before broaching the subject again.

No sooner had we removed our gear from the plane did an odd-looking 4x4 truck appear. The hurricane must have rolled it over several times, crunching the cab into the doors. To operate it, someone took a saw and chopped the roof off. It was now a safari jeep. At least they could get to the seats.

"Hey," the driver said, standing up in the cab. "We handle the maintenance for the federal buildings and were told to come and get you guys. Toss your gear in the back, and the four of you jump in. Two other trucks are coming for the rest of you."

I spotted them as they cruised through the gate and entered the tarmac.

"Take these," the passenger said, tossing us loaded shotguns.

"Is it that bad?" I asked.

"Yeah," he replied. "All the inmates have been let out of jail. It's prison rules now. You'll be the only uniformed police anyone has seen. The military is staying at the airport. It's up to you guys to calm things down."

Ralphie raised his eyebrows and glanced at me.

"We need to travel in packs," the driver said.

"Make sure any weapons you have are ready. People are desperate."

I gave orders to the rest of the team to ready weapons. When we were all loaded, the three vehicles took off in a single file, men hanging out the sides with shotguns and AR15s.

Along the route, we got an eyeful. I watched as people streamed out of a large store with T.V.s on their shoulders, throwing them in the back of a car. They didn't mind us. Yet.

We had to dodge a U.S. Coast Guard cutter as we turned a corner. It looked strange this far inland. It had run aground. I knew for sure someone was gonna lose their job on that one.

On the main road, what used to be hotels were now garbage dumps. Locals climbed over the piles, picking through the debris for anything they could sell. People were everywhere, looking for a chance to jump anyone or anything that might have something of value.

We eventually arrived safely at the U.S. Courthouse.

"Where are we going to sleep?" I asked the driver.

"Inside the courthouse," he said coldly.

I put my hands on my hips. "Okay, men. Let's set up camp inside. I need a perimeter of security right now."

As we worked on that, I learned the DEA's SWAT team had gotten there moments before us. They had secured the U.S. Attorney's Office. That was a huge load off our backs.

The U.S. Attorney for the Virgin Islands arrived after the camp and security were in place. He had a local judge with him, who swore us in as Deputy U.S. Marshals. Effectively, we would be the only police officers on the island. What would have happened to us if we had shot someone before being sworn in? I didn't want to know.

Before we left to begin securing more federal property, Ralphie, the former Marine, took down the tattered American flag and raised a new one we had brought from the states. As a former Marine he wanted to ensure a new flag was flying high before we began operations.

Symbolically, it told the population that the U.S. government was here and in control of this building. It sent a message of strength.

"I gotta admit when Ralphie did that, he motivated the hell outta me."

It was close to noon when we moved out. All of us were strapped with armor and weapons. With everything checked and double-checked, we got down to business.

The first task was inspecting the boats that had washed up on the lawn. In talking to the maintenance personnel, they explained that many locals lived in boats. They had thought they'd be safe if they put out to sea. They were wrong.

I scanned the property for a place to start. This federal building sat on the ocean. As such, there was debris everywhere.

Finding a body in the first boat we checked out didn't take long. And our day had just begun.

Working in teams, we marked which boats contained remains and the coroner team. Right outside was a makeshift morgue. It wasn't a great solution, just the only one available.

Because the bodies had not been there long, they weren't badly decomposed.

After each boat was cleared, we spray-painted a large red X on the outside. This saved other search teams from extra work.

By the day's end, we were hot and tired. We returned to our camp and dined on MREs (Meals Ready to Eat). Since most of us had been in the military, it wasn't a hardship. I actually liked them. Honestly though, I would always try and trade the ones with the ham slice.

My men had put plastic over everything because the water damage would soon turn to mold. To prevent us from getting sick, we covered everything up. Sure, it was hard for stuff to dry, but we weren't there to remodel. Our job was to restore order.

As I lowered my head on my pack, I stared at the ceiling. With no windows in the room, a glow stick gave us enough light to move around. It made the scene eerie. I felt for my loaded gun to give me some comfort. I learned in the military to sleep with my weapon.

Eventually, I closed my eyes and fell into a deep sleep.

Chapter 8

1996 Olympics, Atlanta, Georgia

After several days of searching for survivors, securing the federal building, and taking inventory of our equipment and supplies, we were ordered to secure the shipping docks so FEMA (the Federal Emergency Management Agency) could bring shipments in consisting of food, tarps for roofs, generators, and vehicles.

Ultimately, we had no trouble clearing the area and making it secure for the first shipment to arrive. Then, we signaled the boats waiting offshore to come in and start offloading.

Once we felt FEMA had everything under control, we went across the island to check on the disaster field office (the headquarters for FEMA operations), only we ran into more than we'd bargained for.

My partner and I had just sent our men to various hot spots when we received a call that a Burger King was being looted. With just the two of us, we diverted our route and headed that way.

Spotting the restaurant from a distance, I slowed the truck to a stop. Sure enough, the individuals had broken the locks and were stealing all the supplies. I gunned the truck and stopped near the back entrance. For a moment, the looters were confused. This gave us a chance to go inside and find the manager; thank God he had already escaped.

As we came back outside, a mob of fifteen men surrounded us. Each one carried clubs and weapons. One tough guy held a gun. I looked over at Ralphie, and he read my mind. It was time for Plan B.

We both did an immediate assessment of the situation and knew our original plan wasn't going to work. We slowly eased away from the gang and back to the truck.

In law enforcement, you must always calculate the risks and odds of survival. Sure, we could have taken a few of them. Maybe the rest would have run the other way. But we were so close; all they had to do was take a step forward and double tap us with their clubs, and we'd be gone. That would make our colleagues back in New York don a black armband for a week. I had no desire to have future recruits study the death of Tony Losito, analyzing how they could've done things differently.

Once we were safely in the truck, we drove to the airport and collected a dozen soldiers. When our new posse returned, the looters were gone. Like us, they knew when to fold 'em.

***

St. Thomas was experiencing several serious issues as a result of the hurricane. One of them was electricity. No one had any.

Thieves took full advantage by stripping poles and electrical equipment of copper wire. As I said, it was prison rules. People grabbed anything they could get their hands on.

The original two weeks we were told lasted a lot longer. We were there for a full month. Eventually, the boats were towed off the property, and things started returning to normal. However, we did have some recurring problems.

One of them was the dock. Once FEMA arrived, they had some folks who seemed capable of securing the offloading of supplies and the storage area. However, looters soon infiltrated the dock. Supplies walked off. Generators went missing. Four vehicles that were supposed to be used to deliver supplies evaporated in the steamy tropical air. It was maddening. Left me wondering where the hell they could have gone, it was an island.

Left with no choice, we pulled men away from securing the island to work back on the docks.

Once the dock was re-secured, the bad guys shifted strategies. They began attacking the FEMA crews and supplies as they delivered the goods. Confident we had good security at the docks, I pulled my men off and began escorting FEMA personnel around the island.

Each day we drove to the Disaster Field Office, or DFO as it was referred to too, which was located in one of the few existing hotels. They instructed us on who, when, and where we were to protect, and we would then grab some water and take off.

By now, the many good upstanding locals knew we were there to protect them; the percentage that had been looting knew we were serious if trouble continued. But now, we had reinforcements and a group of other law enforcement officers who flew in to assist.

As things started to improve, the U.S. government wanted us to support the local vendors. When the electricity came back on and stayed on, businesses set up shop again. They needed to make money so the economy could revitalize. Our counterparts that managed the food safety program told us, "Hey, we know you've been sticking to your MREs. But we think it's safe now if you'd like to go out and eat on the economy."

I drove to a small restaurant and bought some jerk chicken. It costs next to nothing, and jerk chicken in the Caribbean is about the best you're going to get.

Unfortunately, that day, unbeknownst to me, the manager even threw in some free helicobacter pylori—H-pylori, for short, the bacteria that causes ulcers. It comes from contaminated food.

Although, I didn't know it for a day or so. That's when my stomach felt like it wanted to explode. Ralphie felt the same. I wouldn't wish that pain on anyone.

We gutted out the pain for another couple of weeks until our jobs were done. When we arrived back home, I tried walking up the five stories to my Manhattan apartment, but I just couldn't make it. Instead, I fell down the stairs, immobilized. The feeling caused pain that shot up my chest; it felt like a heart attack was surely on the menu that day.

Amy, my girlfriend, rushed to help me. She asked if I needed some soup. Our apartment was directly above the "Soup Nazi," the one made famous by Seinfeld.

"No," I croaked. "Just get me to a doctor."

They showed me images of a nasty worm-like creature working its way around my digestive tract, that loved drilling holes through my stomach, which meant I now had an ulcer. After a few weeks of medicine and relaxation, I was back on my watch. But I was pretty sure I had a new partner in my gut.

***

Upon returning to the office, I discovered the Sheikh's long trial was over. He was convicted and eventually sentenced to life in prison without parole. He later died in 2017.

For me, life cruised along easily until 1996.

That's when the Olympics celebrated its one hundred years of international competition. Atlanta, Georgia, was the site of this massive event.

I was assigned a detail of twelve officers and agents to go down there from New York to provide law enforcement and security support for all the federal buildings and personnel around the Olympic venues. I was to stay in Atlanta for two weeks before being replaced by a fresh wave of officers.

Upon arrival, I was met by my assigned driver, Officer Bo Tuck Johnson. He was a good ole boy from Covington, Georgia. Bo had been a captain on the police force in Covington until his retirement a few years earlier, a place where the T.V. series In the Heat of the Night had been filmed. He was there during all the filming, so he had plenty of stories. Trust me, he had stories.

Because he'd served a long career in the Air Force, he wanted to get his ten years with the feds so he could receive a second retirement. The Federal Protective Service, with no age limit, was just what he was looking for.

108

Bo was a slick-sleeved cop. That meant he had no rank. But that was perfect for him; he didn't want a rank or management responsibility. He'd been a captain and didn't want that anymore. He just wanted to hang out and draw a paycheck, waiting until he could tap two retirements.

The first time I met Bo, he had a cinnamon toothpick dangling out of the corner of his mouth.

"I hear you're from New Yawk," he said.

I found myself captivated, staring, and wondering how the hell the toothpick stayed in perfect position while he spoke. It never fell out. Amazing, I thought to myself.

"Yes, Mr. Johnson," I replied. "I'm from New York."

"Please, you can call me Bo. I was told to take good care of you."

As a New Yorker, I get majorly suspicious whenever someone says something like that.

"What do you mean, take good care of me?"

"I heard you're in very tight with the big boss in New Yawk," he said, adjusting his toothpick.

"That's why I'm going to take good care of you."

This was a little after seven in the morning. We had just mustered for the turnout, roll call. With the men headed to their assignments, I was left to supervise everything.

"You ever eat ham hock for breakfast? Or had a thick cup of chock drained through a dirty old sock?" he asked me.

"What…, wait, What? No, Bo, I haven't." "What the hell are you talking about?"

"You mean to tell me you've never had a piece of ham with the bone in the center of it or a delicious black coffee strained through an old sock southern style?"

"No, Bo. I'm a native New Yorker. When we eat breakfast in New York, we have coffee made in a legitimate coffee maker, with ham, eggs, and cheese on a roll. They pump us out fast at the deli because usually, about fifty construction workers are waiting behind us in line. If you want ham with a bone, you go and sit down at a fancy restaurant. As for me, I don't have that kind of time."

"Awww, come on," he said. "You're in the deep South. Do like we do, Brother. I'm going to take you for a goooood old Southern breakfast."

For some reason, he liked to draw out the O's, making the word last twenty seconds.

I sighed. Thought to myself, well, he's probably right. I needed to blend in and not be so uptight.

"Okay," I said, "let's go to breakfast.

He fired up the patrol car.

"I'm going to take you to this special place that only a few locals know about. It's a real backwoods kind of joint. When we get there, I'm going to get you that ham hock with a bone in the center, some fried eggs, and that delicious cup of coffee strained through a dirty old sock they've been using for years. The man frying up your eggs he's going to look like Brutus from the Popeye cartoons. Just don't stare too hard, he gets the Brutus reference all the time, and he doesn't like it."

"And check this out, you're going to get some delicious chock served to you by a nice young lady wearing a wife-beater t-shirt, stains, and all. Oh, and she's pregnant "to boot." She's gonna strain that chock through the dirty sock, and it'll be the best coffee you ever tasted. You'll see."

Memories of H-pylori went through my mind. Honestly, it's another one of those times that we say in law enforcement, "I'm concerned." You see, we never say we're scared; we say we're concerned. Know what I mean.

At this point, I am tense, saying in my head, "Really, I really need to go through this? I could just buzz back a banana and southern peach, and I'm outta here."

We ended up driving ten minutes outside of downtown Atlanta, pulling up to a country-type restaurant. Bo opened the screen door and walked in. He'd only taken two steps when the place erupted. "There's Bo!" Everyone wanted to greet him like he was Elvis. And, of course, he knew everyone. When they saw me in a police uniform, the celebration suddenly stopped. Holy crap, I thought to myself, I'm dead. Like they could read, I was straight from "New Yawk" and don't trust this guy going through their heads.

"Who's that with you, Bo?" a goateed truck driver asked; the concern was written all over his face—at least, between the tattoos. The crowd grew silent and nervous.

"Just stay with me, boy," he whispered as I lagged behind. "I got you on this."

I quickly scanned the place, locating the first few targets to drop. It was exactly as he had promised. It looked like a place cops walked into and disappeared forever. I "felt" for my gun, just making sure it was still there.

"This is my boy Tony from New Yawk City," he announced, slapping his hand on my shoulder.

An uneasy murmur ran through the crowd.

He leaned over and whispered, "We're going to sit in the rear with our backs against the wall, so if they come at us, we've got a fighting chance."

"Bo," I angrily whispered back, "why did you take me to a place that I need to have a fighting chance to eat my freaking breakfast? I don't really need to eat breakfast that bad. I'll eat a banana, and "swig" back a couple of raw eggs. Honestly, don't need a lot of food to function. We're not competing at the Olympics. We're just working the security. I don't want to be sitting down and eating ham hock, really?"

Before I could say another word, the young lady in a wife-beater t-shirt showed up. The only detail Bo had left out was the cigarette hanging from her mouth. As she seated us and poured coffee, I looked past her to the 300-pound Brutus in the kitchen making the food. He had a cigar clenched between his teeth.

When she left, I turned to Bo. "The health department would have a field day in here."

He leaned back and laughed. "Hell, Tony, that's why this place is outside the city limits. There's no health inspector out here in the country. At least, not any that live to tell about it." I placed my hand over my face and looked down, thinking, why the hell did I let him bring me here.

Soon, a plate of ham hocks, grits, eggs, and toast landed in front of me. When I looked down, I had never seen a breakfast like that before. Honestly, it looked good. As I dug in cautiously, I have to admit, it was one of the best, greasiest meals I'd ever enjoyed. I could feel it sliding through my digestive tract as I sat there. And the coffee had a strong kick, just like it was strained through a dirty old sock. With the coffee and food blending together, I felt like an alien was growing inside me. My H-pylori had to be overjoyed. It tasted delicious, though, and on the way out, I grabbed a toothpick just like Bo.

When we slid back into the car, Bo pounded his belly and said, "Now, wasn't that good?"

"You know," I replied, "that place was just like you'd described. Even the cook, Brutus, was spot on."

"He's a great cook," Bo said. "That's for sure. I'll have to take you back for lunch. Brutus takes your hamburger patty and puts it in his armpit. Then he clamps down to his side hard and flattens it out some more."

"That's gross!" I cried. "Insane and illegal!"

"Maybe. But you should see how he makes donuts."

I couldn't tell if he was kidding or serious. But I felt like I was living out a scene from the movie Deliverance.

It was time to get back to business. "Now we're going to check one of our buildings," I said. "Let's go to the Social Security office."

We headed there and found nothing going on. He drove around the building twice before finding a deserted spot at the rear. As he parked and shut off the engine, he launched the driver's seat back.

"What are you doing?" I asked.

"Tony, we just ate a big breakfast. It's time for a break."

"But we haven't done any work yet."

"Yeah, but we always take a break after breakfast; that's why it's called break the fast. The fast is over. It's time for a break, a gooooooood break."

I realized my initial suspicions were correct. I needed to pop this charade. "Bo, have you been told to keep me away from the operations and let the ground pounders handle everything? You know, make sure I don't interfere in anything or see what the local agents are doing?"

"Tony, if you don't want to take a break, I won't take one."

Just what I thought. "I've got a new deal for you. You can drive me where I want when I want, or I'm getting out of this car and calling a cab. When I turn in the expenses for two weeks of cabs, I'm going to write 'Bo Tuck Johnson was busy taking a good break' on the form. Then, I'll let you do the explaining."

At that very moment, a miracle occurred. Bo suddenly decided he wanted a second retirement. That meant being a driver, not a boss. Once he understood this arrangement, we got along fine. Which was good because the last place I wanted to be when a bomb exploded was in the car taking a break.

**

The Olympics lasted for three weeks. We worked security in and around the venue to ensure everything was protected and in order. I also had the honor of conducting security at the Carter Presidential Library. However, my assignment required my specific group to arrive two weeks early. Since we were just about to finish our tour of duty, Bo decided to raise a new restaurant up the flagpole for lunch one day.

"Tony, it's lunchtime. I'm going to take you to this great place to eat. You like catfish?"

"Bo, I told you, I'm from New York City. There's no catfish there, at least none that you want to eat. And you already know we don't fish in those rivers. We go to the supermarket to buy our food, or maybe a restaurant or a deli. No, I've never had catfish before."

"Alright, Tony. I'm going to show you where we can make some combs for your hair."

That made no sense, but I let him drive me several minutes to the outskirts of town. We arrived in front of a pink building with a sign swinging by one chain. As the wind spun it around, I noticed the name was Jessabelle's.

I stepped out of the car to hear gravel crunching beneath my feet. Nothing was paved anywhere. And the road leading to the place was dirt and gravel. This was out in the boonies.

I walked in behind Bo. From the décor, I figured the place had been set up circa 1955. Its clientele appeared to be the same desperados from the breakfast joint, all wearing wife-beater t-shirts or similar attire.

A waitress approached and said, "Bo Tuck!" I stood there while they hugged for a little too long and a little too close for my taste.

"Rhonda, this here is my friend Tony from New Yawk City. He's never had catfish."

"Oh my," she said, brushing the hair away from her eyes while giving me the up-down. "A first timer. I like that. Rhonda will take good care of you, mister." She sucked on her index finger for a few seconds before heading back to the kitchen.

Bo and I made small talk until Rhonda reappeared with one plate. "You'll always remember your first, Tony." She sucked on her finger again, staring at me as she went to another table.

I looked at the food. There were small slices of catfish deep-fried in seasoned cornmeal.

"Tony, these are the appetizers. You eat them like finger food. Dip them in this tartar sauce or this cocktail sauce here. Some folks use ketchup, but they don't last long around here."

I tried them. They were pretty good, like a cross between fish and chicken. Right behind that were two big plates of catfish. I mean, the entire fish—head, and whiskers too. Each one was surrounded by a tall pile of coleslaw and hushpuppies scattered everywhere. It was a feast for a king.

"Tony, the meat falls off the bone. And you pick off the fins and use them like a comb if you want. Now, we Southerners eat the "fins." They're crunchy."

I picked off a piece of fish, thinking of my new ulcer.

A side plate had Vidalia onions, pickles, and butter for the stack of fresh bread they left in a cloth-covered basket. Good luck chasing down a bad guy with this camped out in your stomach.

Before I knew what was happening, Bo reached over and grabbed a whole onion with his hand.

"What are you going to do with that?" I asked.

"Eat it, you Yankee."

I watched in horror as he bit into the onion like an apple, chewed it up, and swallowed the remains. It brought back memories of my younger brother eating sticks of butter while sitting a foot from the T.V. My mother would yell at him, "Don't sit so close. The rays will give you cancer!" It turned my stomach to see my brother eat a stick of butter. Seeing Bo eat that onion, I couldn't decide which was worse.

He begged and begged, but he couldn't get me to bite into an onion. I did eat the catfish, however, and surprisingly, just like my ham hock breakfast, it was delicious. And I did get one fin down. Hopefully, it will slip past my ulcer.

When the bill came, Bo picked up the tab. It came to a little over $10. I left a five for the tip, ashamed I didn't leave more, as I was pleasantly surprised by how good it really was. Needless to say, that was my last good Southern experience.

Once the Olympic games started, I was scheduled to rotate out shortly after. However, there were too many bomb threats being called in. My boss told me to keep my team in Atlanta and stay one more week. We patrolled the grounds where the games were held and the federal buildings around it. This included Centennial Park and other key venues due to numerous concerns. We worked hard for seven more days without incident before punching out and heading home to New York City.

I felt good that nothing happened during our watch. And with the second wave taking over for us, I knew the Olympic security detail was in good hands.

On July 27, 1996, just four days after we had rotated out, a bomb exploded, killing two and injuring 111. Another man died of a heart attack.

I jumped on the phone in New York and assisted our people in acquiring supplies, securing federal facilities, and assisting in whatever way I could. The crews were on top of everything, some "triaging" the victims. Thankfully none of our team was injured.

We called out the K9s and checked everything. No additional bombs were found, and not one federal property was damaged. But that didn't lessen the pain the victims' families went through. We helped in every way we could, especially assisting the FBI and local agencies. With hundreds of police on full alert, the Olympics went on without another incident.

As for the murderer, suspicion initially fell on Richard Jewell, a security guard who had found a package. He'd been in the process of clearing people away when the bomb went off. Both the FBI and the media drilled down on him, sweating him out in public.

Eventually, the FBI turned from Jewell and focused on Eric Rudolph. Rudolph was connected to other bombs as well. Based on interviews with Rudolph's family and friends, the FBI assumed he was hiding in the Appalachian wilderness, a place he was familiar with from his youth.

Rudolph eluded the police for approximately five years before a rookie cop found the killer foraging in a dumpster at four in the morning. He took a plea deal to avoid the death penalty and is spending his days in the ADX Florence Supermax. Richard Jewell settled his lawsuits against the media that slammed him. He died in 2007 at the age of forty-four.

All of this is another example of a cop punching in and doing his job. The rookie cop checks out a possible burglary, and Richard Jewell finds a suspicious bag and saves lives. It always amazes me how effective this strategy is.

**

I had put in two years when I started looking for opportunities to become a Special Agent. Special Agents had the best and most sought-after jobs and retirement because the job paid more than other administrative retirements. They also made double what I was making in the Federal Protective Service.

After searching for months through the job postings, it was clear the Federal Protective Service didn't have any job openings available. That pushed me to look at other agencies.

I "d developed a good relationship with Danny McGregor at the U.S. Department of Housing and Urban Development (HUD), Office of Inspector General. This was the overwatch law enforcement arm of HUD. I would see him weekly as he came through the lobby of the federal building. He would always be in his raid gear, coming or going to another event.

Over coffee and lunch, Danny regaled me with stories about his agency's mission of fighting guns, gangs, and drugs in and around public housing all over New York and New Jersey. He also told me they were looking for new agents to join a new mission called "Operation Safe Home," targeting guns, gangs, and drugs in public and assisted housing.

I went with him to his office one day to meet the Special Agent in Charge. He spoke with me and encouraged me to apply. I was eventually hired, leaving the Federal Protective Service, which ironically was located (on the 17th floor) for the HUD Office of Inspector General (on the 34th floor). I was moving on up— literally.

But if I thought I had experienced an adventurous life so far, I was underestimating everything.

This job would blow the doors off anything I'd ever imagined.

It was time to pony up.

Chapter 9

The Office of Inspector General

It was May 1997 when I took the elevator to the thirty-fourth floor and started my first day at the HUD Office of Inspector General New York Office of Investigations. Because the government is so massive, one investigatory agency can't supervise all of them. That's why each agency has its own Inspector General. The "IG," as it's often called, is responsible for ensuring its "mother agency" complies with all laws, regulations, and procedures. If someone defrauds a program or is suspected of wrongdoing, the IG steps in and investigates.

Another part of the "IG's" responsibility is to protect the people and assets of that agency. It's much like the Federal Protective Service protecting federal employees and property. Only HUD's IG maintained oversight over its agency programs and ran a special program that watched over the federally funded housing developments and other properties.

There were two sides to the HUD IG during my time there: white-collar investigations and the violent crimes section. A typical white-collar investigation might involve someone receiving a rental subsidy, the government pays most if not all their rent, yet they have stated they're unemployed. Still, in reality, they have a great job. In other words, they've lied in their application to obtain a federal subsidy they were not entitled to had they told the truth. These types of cases alone added up to hundreds of thousands of dollars that the American taxpayer has been defrauded. Our job was to try and stop it.

Unfortunately, it was too tempting to steal. Some individuals found a way to double down even further on the scheme to defraud by signing the lease, getting the subsidy then subletting the subsidized apartment they are supposed to be living in over to another tenant. "Power Brokers!" it's unbelievable. This was a double violation of the program. Other cases involved mortgage fraud and related programs or grant fraud cases. That's where the white-collar side of the IG came in. They investigated the situation and conducted enforcement action.

As for me, I was slotted into the violent crimes section. Our mission was Operation Safe Home, which involved combatting guns, gangs, and drugs in and around public and assisted housing in the New York and New Jersey metropolitan areas. It was kicked off in 1994 by Vice President Al Gore. The purpose of the program was to provide safe, decent, and sanitary housing for folks who lived in HUD-subsidized developments. The prominent locations we were concerned with were large cities where crime in these areas was extremely high.

Our job was to go out to these cities and areas and recruit state or local law enforcement to work with us to combat violent crime in and around public housing. Once we had the assets in place, we picked a development and worked until it was free of corruption and safe for the residents. Then, we'd move to the next one.

But before I could do anything, my boss called me in to see her. She asked me to close the door.

"Tony, I need you to conduct an internal investigation of a new Special Agent. He's accused of making false statements on his application." She slid the file to me.

"This guy is two desks down," I said. "Are you kidding me?"

"You know we eat our own young," she replied.

"That's how it is. He might be investigating you one day."

I went back to my desk and stared at my colleague—the suspect. It was a weird feeling.

I investigated the man for a week before clearing him. The person complaining had some type of beef and wanted him to suffer a long internal investigation. It didn't work because he was as clean as they come.

With the internal investigation complete, my boss brought me back to discuss collateral duty. Collateral duties were designed to complete critical extra mission-related jobs around the office; everyone was expected to take at least one collateral duty. Law enforcement doesn't always run in a straight line. It takes a lot to run a large mission, and your collateral duty runs alongside your regular job. Sometimes collateral duties could take up most of your time if you weren't assigned the right one.

My boss handed me a list of collateral duties to choose from.

"Pick something off this list that you want, and I'll assign you that duty."

I opened the folder and saw that almost everything was crossed off.

"The only one left was technical electronics surveillance agent," I looked up and said, "What happened to the other duties?"

"Look," she said, moving her chair closer to the desk.

"We have guys in here who can't even run a remote control, much less their own VCR. No way they can handle complicated electronics like this job calls for. That's why I'm thrilled you want to be a technical electronics surveillance agent. Great choice, Tony. You'll do a fine job; thank you for stepping up."

In law enforcement, we have one word for what just happened to me: voluntold.

When you're told to volunteer and don't have a choice from the start, they make you feel like you did.

Such was life working for the government. But the joke was on them because I ultimately worked on some unbelievable cases. And I made myself incredibly valuable to HUD and other law enforcement agencies.

HUD sent me to over thirty different schools to get the proper training, including the most sought-after undercover cover agent school. There was a two-year wait on average for this school, but somehow, I got right in after my immediate supervisor made a couple of calls. I learned how to operate as an undercover government agent. The collateral duty required me to work in an undercover capacity to carry out covert assignments.

Then, I went to a school for advanced technical electronic surveillance which included body wiring, advanced installations, telephone training, basic electricians training, specialized equipment training, lock picking, and covert entries.

I climbed telephone poles to tap lines and crawled through ceilings to drop in an eye-in-the-sky camera. I learned from former covert agents the critical techniques needed to do the job. I even attended the DEA's highly prized advanced technical electronics surveillance school. The training was incredible.

Once I was completely educated, I proceeded to inventory our technical supply storage room. All we had to start with were two items: a Polaroid camera and a Nagra reel-to-reel recorder.

The Nagras were ancient history. In the seventies, agents taped them to a person's back and ran the mic to the mole's chest. The bulky devices were first used in Hollywood to record actors for later insertion into the movie. But this was 1997. Even the lowest criminals would hug another person while checking their back for a Nagra.

Then I picked up the Polaroid camera.

"I learned how to use this in one of the schools," I told my boss.

She got excited.

"I knew that would come in handy. How do you use it in covert operations?"

"Let's say we're undercover and see the target walking down the street to meet another suspect. I'd walk up to the suspect, hold the camera twelve inches from his face, and take his picture. The flash blinds him briefly, for a second, allowing me to get away fast."

Her expression dropped.

"That sounds dangerous. And I guess he now knows who you are."

She studied my expression.

"Are you joking?"

"What else do you expect me to say about this barren desert of technical gadgets I'm staring at? Even Sherlock Holmes had a magnifying glass. I've got a Polaroid camera and a twenty-year-old Nagra."

She ran a hand through her hair.

"Maybe we can get some money. What's the first thing you need?"

"A surveillance vehicle!" I told her I needed a high-tech surveillance vehicle to conduct covert operations. I laid out all the details.

Soon, the IG searched between its couch cushions and located $135,000 for a state-of-the-art vehicle. I went to California and worked with the company on the assembly line every day until it was finished. When I finally took delivery of the unit, it was magnificent. It had everything I needed.

While I can't mention some of its best features, one of them was a separate heater and A/C unit. This one was so quiet that if a person stood next to the van, they had no idea someone was inside. Without the unit, and the cool air it put out, the air from our lungs would fog up the glass on the inside—a sure giveaway. And that's not overlooking the need to be comfortable while spending hours inside a tiny space, especially during brutal winters and blazing summers.

I was so happy with the new vehicle that I couldn't wait to wreck it. I had already scouted out several pipe bollards that would do nicely.

One afternoon, I took the van out and banged it around a little. Not too much. Just enough to lend some New York City street credibility to it. Then I placed old stickers all over it, while making sure to leave dirty food wrappers on the dashboard and front seat. By the time I was finished, I had the entire vehicle looking like any average contractor truck in New York City.

The next task was to paint the sides with my "cover." I had selected to be an electrician. This worked with the wires and supplies I carried around. The name I selected was Johnson Electric, after Paul Johnson. His watch ended on April 19, 1995, in the bombing of the Alfred P. Murrah Federal Building in Oklahoma City. Paul was a special agent for HUD's IG and died with thirty-four other HUD employees. I felt it was a nice tribute to a man whose name would carry forward his mission.

My final touch was to drive it to an area and leave it under a large maple tree for a week. This allowed the leaves and bird droppings to infuse into the paint. When I went to fetch it, I realized my masterpiece was ready. No way anyone would ever figure this out for an undercover truck.

Proud of my new baby, I parked it in the garage so my boss could check it out. She came down, walked around it, and slapped her cheeks with her hands.

"What have you done?! Are you crazy?"

"Yes," I said. "Isn't it beautiful?"

She thought I'd lost my mind until I explained what I'd learned in school. Eventually, she got it. But, at first, it was a tough sell.

***

One of my first undercover surveillance jobs was at a mortgage company. The white-collar special agents suspected the company was setting up fraudulent HUD loans. The scam involved fake people taking out a loan on behalf of real folks who didn't know they'd taken one out. Obviously, the paper trail was laxer back then.

Eventually, the loans defaulted. The bank foreclosed on the home, never knowing the person didn't exist. It was a neat scam that netted a ton in mortgage origination fees.

The agents were able to bust a secretary for the president of one of the mortgage companies. She met them at dinner and cut a deal, providing us valuable inside information.

Based on that, the agents obtained a search warrant. But first, a female agent and I visited the office during business hours and talked with the president. He thought one of his people was in trouble, so he didn't consider us a threat. While my partner talked with him, I looked around and "studied" his office, taking note of everything. I was also wearing a body cam that took still photos. I moved around to get the entire scene.

Back at my office, I downloaded the pictures and recreated the president's office. Then, I targeted something the secretary had told us he never moved: an unused CPU that sat on his desk.

After studying the CPU, I bought one exactly like it and ripped out the guts. With a clean palette to work with, I put a camera and mic inside. Even though the camera was run by a battery pack, I hooked it into the electronics so I could plug it into the wall. I wanted to keep it running in case I couldn't get back in there fast.

The search warrant we already had in hand allowed me to sneak in and get everything set up. However, they had excellent locks and security. It would be a lot of work to break through. The odds of getting caught were high. To counter this risk, I spent a month working on the maintenance man. I finally convinced him to give me the keys. That made it easy to slip in at two a.m.

Dressed in black and with a tiny flashlight between my teeth, I wired up the president's office with mics. Then I switched out CPUs, being careful to spray fake dust everywhere. I needed it to look like it had been sitting there for a year. After inspecting my handiwork, I plugged it in. It worked perfectly.

As I headed to the exit, someone drove up to the office. They walked up to the door but couldn't get in. I had locked it—but not all the way since I was inside. I quickly looked for a place to hide.

I peeked out from behind a curtain to see a guy exit the vehicle and come to the main entrance. He seemed drunk because he dropped his keys twice. Suddenly, a woman in the passenger seat waved him back to the car. He turned and stared at her for a few seconds, dropped his keys again, and decided she offered more than whatever he needed in the office.

Ah, love. It's the salve of undercover work.

He rejoined his girl and took off. That was enough for me to grab my tools and race to the door, locking up in record time.

As I sat in my van, I knew I had almost blown a four-month investigation. The president would've been tipped off and blamed the underlings for the fraud. With a good attorney, it might have worked.

Instead, we took him down. Then we hit four more mortgage companies he turned us on to. It was a huge bust; one I would've never taken part in unless I had been the technical surveillance agent for the IG. Pretty sweet!

***

Over time, I was able to build up the surveillance inventory to over a million dollars of state-of-the-art equipment. I had the latest of everything, including a slew of remotely activated devices. I was able to surveil conversations and obtain video from alternate locations.

Today's technology is far more advanced. But back then, I could enter an office, put devices in place, and remove the old ones in a matter of minutes. These were brilliant inventions.

Other technology I had consisted of a selection of night scopes, advanced tape-recording systems, and long-distance video cameras. As I built a technological empire, I set up a workbench with tools. This allowed me to create anything I needed. I was a real-life Q, like in those James Bond movies. It was a great collateral duty that was turning full-time. The agents constantly called me to support their cases, asking for surveillance videos and recordings for their ongoing cases. The demand grew very large and soon became all I was doing, and I was operating undercover full-time.

***

Even more agents and local departments heard about what I was able to provide and how good my techniques were, and I was pulled in all sorts of directions. I had earned a solid reputation. I was soon tasked by other police departments to assist in their operations because I had such a good cover vehicle and appearance.

One job involved a family who was supposedly living in the apartment but had actually sublet it to another family. To do the job right, I placed a camera in the family picture hanging on the wall (the family that was supposed to be living there), setting the lens in the father's eye. The agents soon racked up another conviction.

Another investigation involved putting a camera in a doll's eye. That nabbed a narcotics ring.

Many of the investigations involved people who had turned and were working for the government. They were the only ones who could get the evidence needed to convict. I wired up the young and old alike. It was always concerning because one mistake on my part and the person could be injured… or worse.

One interesting investigation involved a married manager for a local contracted housing office who had impregnated his girlfriend. Normally, HUD wouldn't care. That was his business. However, his pregnant girlfriend worked for him. Because she had morning sickness, she had used up all her sick time. When she needed more time off, he simply approved her timecard, showing she was there most of her nine-month pregnancy. Defrauding a federally funded program. Too many people complained to let this go, it had to be addressed.

The agents wanted me to catch him in the act approving the timecards and speaking with the girlfriend employee in question.

That meant crawling through a ceiling to drop in an eye in the sky just outside the target's office. It was risky, but I was sure I could do it.

After scouting out the area, I calculated the cleaning service's time along with the security guard's rotation. Crunching some numbers, I came up with a solid game plan.

As always, I had to be careful with anyone outside my little group. You learn that anyone can tip off the target. Who knows who knows who?

By this time, I was a pro—confident and experienced. I figured fifteen minutes in and out. It would be like a Mission: Impossible job. After it was over, I planned on sharing a beer with the agents. They might even buy.

Early one morning, I inserted myself between the cleaners and the security guard. Then, I climbed up through pipes in a telephone closet. After reaching the top, I crawled over the ceiling grid. Yet something happened that I didn't plan on.

The subcontractors who had put in the ceiling never assumed it needed to carry the weight of a human being. Two tiles collapsed, and yup, I fell through.

Luckily, I didn't get hurt. Once I collected myself, I saw the floor was covered with ceiling tile debris. It would take a vacuum cleaner to get this up. And there was a large hole in the ceiling. No way the target would miss this mess.

When you're in the middle of a crisis, the best thing you can do is stop and spend a minute carefully sorting out your options. For me, the best option was sneaking out of the building, hoping I could dodge the guards. It worked. No one saw me.

My cover as an electrician allowed me to carry in a vacuum cleaner and other tools.

It took five hours to clean up the mess. This included "borrowing" some ceiling tiles from an adjoining tenant as well as installing the camera. I'm not entirely sure how, but I got the job done, and "no one was the wiser."

Eight months later, the target pled guilty. It was another victory for the government.

***

A component of being undercover is truly looking the part. To fit in with the persona of an electrician, I sported a long ZZ Top goatee. I added henna tattoos on the side and back of my shaved head. Sometimes, the tattoos were Japanese writings. I had to get them refreshed regularly by a henna tattoo artist. As a final touch, I had clip-on earrings.

Many times, NYPD confronted me. It might have been that my truck was improperly parked. Or I just looked like a criminal. NYPD and Undercovers had a great symbiotic relationship. I have to admit, NYPD is the best all around, and they were so supportive of my work. Whenever I was confronted, I pulled out my badge and showed it to them. This is called "flipping tin."

Often, the officer would step back, amazed I was an agent.

Usually, you can trust that they will keep quiet about who you are and what you're doing. In some investigations, the target was so valuable or powerful that we couldn't take a chance. They might also be friends with someone who knows someone else, and so on. Or they could harmlessly go and ask why they had an electrician in their place. We never knew what could happen. In those cases, I accepted the parking ticket and dealt with it later.

Another key component of undercover work is backstopping. My identification cards—driver's license, business card, etc., had information that had to line up. Various agencies have super-secure departments that create fake IDs and plug the information into the computer. If a cop runs your license, it comes back, matching your undercover ID.

If I ever had to take a ticket, I would give it to my handler. He would take it to the proper department and get it adjudicated.

Having an undercover ID as a contractor meant that sometimes, people called you up. They would see my truck or ask for a business card. Maybe a cop or security guard might call to check on me. To solve this problem, I set up a phone in the main office that was plugged into an answering machine. Nobody answered the phone.

Occasionally, someone would pull the plug. I continually reminded them, "You guys don't understand how important this is. Please, keep it plugged in!"

Unfortunately, it kept happening. To stop this, I set the phone up inside a locked office.

***

As I have said before, police work means you never know what the day will bring. One tragic incident took place at 26 Federal Plaza—

the same building where I'd had to clear the daycare after the Oklahoma City bombing.

A man was on the ninth floor attending an immigration hearing. He had requested political asylum. Because he might lose, he had been told to bring his luggage with him.

When the judge ruled against the man and said he'd have to go back to Russia, he sprinted full speed toward the window and crashed through it. He landed right outside on the plaza, his body splitting in two. The upper part of his torso went one way, and the bottom portion, including the legs, went in a different direction. It was a loud noise that scared everyone. Very sad and very tragic.

I was in the lobby and avoided the worst of it. Sadly, the pedestrians outside were shocked at the site. They had to deal with what they saw for the rest of their lives.

This just amplifies my previous point: As a cop, each day holds life and death. You just hope that you get home alive at the end of your shift. If that happens, it's a good day.

Chapter 10

"Narco Rangers"

I went in one morning and found a case file on my desk. Between all my surveillance work, I had to handle the cases. I'd been hired for violent crime. That meant conducting investigative fieldwork, presenting cases, and all the administrative work that comes with it. I was also very active working on a variety of narcotics cases which required me to be present to participate in both search and arrest warrants.

Those of us working narcotics were known in the inner circles as "Narco Rangers." That's what law enforcement in the city calls detectives and agents working on special narcotics enforcement operations.

I read the file and saw the problem. Supposedly someone was "pitching" drugs from the fifth floor of a housing development. Pitching drugs is a simple yet effective way to sell narcotics with the least likelihood of getting caught. Here's how it works.

A buyer approaches a man sitting on a bench. The bench is located on the perimeter of the housing development. The bench man is wearing a hoodie. He has his hands in his pockets, likely fingering a weapon. He talks to the buyer, asking questions while sizing him up. The goal is to sniff out a cop or rival gang member. If the buyer receives the approval of this bench man, he's directed to another man located inside the development.

This second man checks out the buyer too. He looks for anything suspicious. If the buyer clears this second man, he may be directed to a third man. If there are only two men, the buyer will be told which window to approach. When I say men, unfortunately, they range in age from as young as fourteen to as old as eighty.

The buyer walks up to a ground-floor apartment window, the one with bars and other security devices. The buyer slips the money through a crack to a man behind the window. Inside the apartment, it's dark. The buyer will be unable to ID anyone.

Once the money is counted, the window man slides the crack back through the crack (no pun intended). Sometimes, they stand away from the window and "pitch it out" to avoid being seen.

Like a national burger chain, these guys have an assortment of drugs. The only thing they lack is an actual menu.

Pitching is primarily done from the ground-level apartments. Not too many dealers are willing to do it from the fifth floor. Why? Because no buyer is going to walk all the way up there with cash. It's too dangerous and even riskier after the buy. It takes far too long to get back down and get away with the drugs in the event the cops are lurking.

Additionally, no telling what other user or seller might pop out from an apartment door and snatch the buyer. When this happens, it's known as a "rip' on the street. It's short for rip-off. A rip is not just dangerous; it's downright embarrassing on the street. And the buyer must do without his fix. A rip means it's just a really bad day.

As I reviewed the details of this case, it was a conundrum. I was going to have to tap all my brain cells to solve this "caper."

First, I found out who was living in the apartment. It was an elderly couple who had either been forced out so drug dealers could operate, or the couple had a relative doing it. Unfortunately, this information didn't add anything to the investigation.

Next, I went undercover and spent a few days scouting the area. I wanted to get a feel for how people moved around and their normal paths of travel. I also needed to scout out places to plant some video cams.

Once I felt I had a handle on the area, I dressed up as a contractor and planted several video cams in exit signs at the end of the hallway in the building. This would catch whoever was going in and out of the suspected apartment. Then, I headed for my surveillance vehicle and settled in for a long night.

Because this was in Little Italy, I had to be careful about "stepping" on someone else's set. A set is an area where other law enforcement is working, like a set in the movie industry. On many of the sets I worked on, there could be up to five other agencies in an undercover capacity. Busting someone or creating a commotion could ruin another agency's special investigation. After all, poachers who shoot at rabbits can scare away big game.

To make sure I wasn't stepping on anyone's "set," I made calls to the agencies in the area. No one was there. So, the coast was clear for me to begin operating.

The video cams I used operated on wireless transmission. I needed to have my magical surveillance vehicle nearby to capture and record the signals.

I went to a fantastic Italian deli nearby on the night of my stakeout. I bought myself a whole spread of Italian food. A sliced hunk of imported prosciutto di Parma. Some homemade lasagna. A semolina roll, a few long pepperoncini, and a pint of steaming tomato sauce to dip the bread in. (Just typing this makes me hungry.) With everything in place, I was set for a long night of surveillance.

Hours ticked by with nothing happening. Then, around 11 p.m., I broke open the dessert—some cherry antacid tablets—and chewed on a few. As I sat in the back of my vehicle studying the signal feeds, something crazy happened. A camera from the top of my truck, which was trained on the building, picked up a white bucket being lowered from about the 10th floor of the building next to my vehicle. It was slowly dropping down on a rope from the fifth floor, and standing on the sidewalk below it was a buyer. I watched as he placed his money in the bucket and raised it. A minute later, the bucket came back down, and the buyer took his product.

Incredible, I thought. The ingenuity of some people never ceases to amaze me.

I left the area that evening and documented my findings. A few days later, we had an undercover narc make some controlled buys from the bucket crew. Finally, we had these hardened criminals. It was time to armor up and take them down.

On the morning of the bust, tensions ran high. Climbing up ten floors carried all sorts of risks. If the dealers were tipped off, they could start raining lead down on us. A few dealers in New York City had been reported to have hand grenades. And these killers could pop out of any door on any floor at any moment. We could easily be ambushed and lose some officers on a mission like this.

After spending a great deal of time laying out our attack plan, we got ready and loaded into the police vans. Inside, we said a prayer and waited for the van to stop.

It seemed like forever to get there, but in reality, it was at most ten minutes. The van I was in stopped, and the signal was given. We slid the door back and ran hard to the building.

All those who were chosen were in prime shape. All of us climbed the ten flights in record time. My heart was pounding as we rammed the door in.

Quickly, we fanned out through the apartment. There on the bed were the two dealers, reaching for something—most likely an AK-47. As we hit the lights, I saw they were reaching for something else: a cane, dentures, and a set of eyeglasses.

It turned out the major dealer lowering the bucket was a seventy-six-year-old woman on social security. Her husband was nearing eighty. Both were close to "kicking the bucket" themselves (no pun intended). They weren't hardened criminals unless you counted their arteries. After we explained how many years they would serve in prison, they gave up the criminals above them, and we were able to get pretty high (okay, pun intended) in the organization. Turns out they needed a way to supplement their Social Security income. You'd think they would be soft older folk; instead, they were hardened tough dealers, and we interrupted their retirement income. They were upset for sure.

Although this was our job. Chalk up another building made safe. At least for a few hours or so until the next crew moves in.

***

In training, we are told while in this role, people (the general public, bad guys, internal affairs…etc..) are watching us from Day One.

"So, don't do anything you wouldn't want your friends and family to see on video or anything that would land your face on the front page of the newspaper. If it raises a question mark in your mind, don't do it."

The integrity of police officers is a vital component of a functional and trusted police force. If the officers can steal or be bribed, we're all done. Chaos and crime will reign.

So, to routinely provide the highest levels of service, all departments conduct integrity tests from time to time. One such test involved collaboration with an integrity unit and department I shall not name. The tests were requested to be conducted in various public housing developments for which I had jurisdiction, so I provided technical support. I was asked to assist with the testing because I had access to housing and high-tech surveillance equipment.

The first set of tests occurred in a New York, New Jersey Metropolitan housing development. I served as the technical electronics surveillance agent. The internal affairs unit and I set up apartments with detectives and officers who comprised families of all ages. Then, we made carefully coordinated ruse 911 calls alleging a domestic disturbance was underway.

Uniformed officers would respond to the calls. The father and kids would leave the room to see if the responding officers took the money lying around the apartment. We went for broke and set out additional items such as pornographic material and jewelry. I had wired the place for sound and video. If the officers took something, the unit would take appropriate action.

I've got to say this was one of the most difficult assignments for me to work on. These are my brothers and sisters. I hated having to do these tests. But all officers and agents know these tests are a routine part of the job. Additionally, most detectives have to do a tour through their internal affairs unit during the life of their career at some point, so they know how it works. And these tests took officers away from real calls. But the difference between our law enforcement agencies and other countries, where bribes are common and accepted, are tests like these.

This operation continued for a year and a half on and off over the months with different apartment units throughout the tri-state area. Incredibly, not one officer took the bait we had out for them. They all acted professionally and with the highest order of professionalism and integrity. I was very proud of them. No wait, I was extremely proud of them, which is why I took the time to tell this story, to tout their solid work and integrity.

However, during one specific set of tests, something completely arbitrary and unforeseen occurred. A neighboring tenant told our fake family they'd had to pay for routine maintenance work. Work that should have been part of the regular maintenance process in the building. So, we set up a scene with an older woman and called maintenance, telling them she needed her A/C unit installed. They were supposed to come in and install it for her for no charge as part of their routine duties.

Instead, they showed up and said, "Listen, I can't put that unit in the window. It's going to take some extra time. Why don't I come back after hours, and I'll take care of that for you?"

"Why can't you do it now?" she asked.

"We're short on time, so we can't do that right now."

"But it's going to be hot all day," she complained.

"I promise I'll be back," they said.

Sure enough, they returned after their shift and said they could get that unit hooked up for only $300. Apparently, the workers had been doing scams like this for years.

Shaking down elderly people on fixed incomes was an evil crime. I have to admit this is exactly why units like mine existed. I enjoyed putting an end to that practice and quick. Needless to say, these two were no longer employed in the housing development after our case evidence was presented. Video is powerful evidence. I always say, "You can't run from what you see on the screen."

***

Being a Narco Ranger was most dangerous when the suspect's building was in the middle of the development, and their apartment was on or near the top floor. Because we are forced to park our units on the perimeter of the development, the bad guys would often have lots of warnings. Add in the time it takes to climb to the top, and they can have their automatic rifles locked and loaded before we can knock and announce.

On one investigation, I had both of those dangerous elements present. We had to carefully plan the raid to ensure our safety.

This was a high-visibility enforcement operation. We didn't have any warrants. Instead, it was an "on view" operation. When we performed high visibility and enforcement operations, each team traveled to its assigned building and took the elevator to the top. The idea is to catch prostitutes soliciting in the halls, drug deals going down, or any other nefarious activity going on that affects the general quality of life in a negative way. The idea was to provide safe, decent, and sanitary housing for those who wanted to live a normal life.

In this instance, any case of wrongdoing we observed we addressed. That's on view, or "in plain view," as it's sometimes called. Think of "shock and awe" in military actions. This is the law enforcement version.

On the appointed day at 2 p.m., the van doors rolled back, and thirty Housing cops, along with twenty-five Special Agents, jumped out and ran to our assigned buildings. Agents were paired up with uniform housing cops.

As I headed toward my assigned building, cabbages and dishes crashed all around me, just narrowly missing my head. The tenants in the building threw all sorts of garbage at us. It wasn't uncommon to have kitchen knives tossed or even appliances thrown out the windows. Just as I came under the awning at the main entrance, a bathroom sink and a brick crashed right next to me. When you hear someone say they threw everything at me except the kitchen sink. Well, they threw the bathroom sink at us.

Unbelievable!

My partner and I sprinted to the elevator. Our plan was to get to the top fast and work our way down. I reached to press a button but realized the tenants had been tipped off. They knew we were coming or just saw us coming. How did I know this? Because someone had spread human feces all over the buttons to prevent us from using them. As I looked around, I realized multiple people had defecated on the elevator floor as well. This was to dissuade us from using the elevator and prevent us from conducting vertical patrols. It was a mess.

With no choice, we started up the stairs. Of course, we lost the element of surprise. And we failed to arrest anyone on that mission.

Back down on the ground, the team assembled. People were still throwing things at us, but it was slowing now that they saw we had stopped making vertical patrols. That's when a few kids ventured outside to watch us.

I went back to the van and grabbed a duffle bag full of stuff. When I made it to the courtyard, two young boys—maybe eight or nine— cautiously approached me on their bikes. One kid said, "What are you carrying?"

I had my gun in a holster on my right thigh. "A nine-millimeter."

"Can I see it?" he asked.

"No, you can't." I had a special lock on my "rig" to prevent anyone from grabbing my weapon. People had tried.

"What's your name?"

"Raheem," he said.

I reached into the bag and pulled out a pamphlet. My boss had instructed me to always pass out the Operation Safe Home pamphlets. The pamphlets described how each tenant was entitled to be safe inside their unit. No one ever took them, but I had to at least try.

"Would you like a pamphlet?" I asked, holding one out.

"What's that?" he asked, ignoring my question, and pointing to an orange shape in my bag.

"It's a basketball," I said excitedly.

"Here, let me give that to you."

"I don't want that," he said, backing away.

"Why not?" I said.

"It's free and full of air."

"Because if I take that basketball from you, by the time I get back to my apartment, put my bike away, and try to get out and play basketball, I'll probably get killed because I took a basketball from 5-O." *(Five-O is a street refence to the old police drama TV show Hawaii Five-O, so Five-O means cops)*

"So, you really don't want a basketball?" I asked, dumbfounded.

"Are you out of your mind?" he said, face scrunched up.

"You might as well hand me a $50 bill right here like I'm a snitch, which I ain't taking that either. All I was asking you was what kind of gun you had on. You guys had better learn just to get the hell out of here."

I put the basketball away and headed back to the van. It was an incredibly eye-opening and sad moment for me. Not only because

146

that kid had refused my gift but because the violence and despair were so entrenched in his DNA. He had grown up with this knowledge. That kid had more street smarts than a normal nine-year-old. All he was trying to do was survive the day. And living in a place where people smear human waste in elevators. How can anyone grow up normal in a place like that?

***

Another investigation took place at the West Brighton houses in Staten Island. The area was gang-controlled and had a terrible drug infestation. It was so bad we received over $1 million in funding to tackle the problem. I was assigned to head the operation for my agency. I gathered a team of NYPD who was already working hard in Staten Island, along with several other Special Agents, to help conduct the operation.

To get some quick results and low-hanging fruit, we made controlled buys and arrested a bunch of dealers. We also nabbed several drug soldiers—the enforcement wing of drug dealers. But my tactics backfired. Soon, the dealers knew the feds were shaking down their crew (a term used for cracking down hard). Overnight, the drug dealers disappeared. This was a problem.

We had a sit-down and discussed the matter. Whenever we conducted enforcement operations, we wore jackets that said Federal Agent on the back. We had also brought in Agents from other government agencies who wanted to help. They wore the same jackets. Telling the criminals that federal agents were involved scared the drug dealers because the prison time in the federal system is so much longer. Our success basically shifted the bad guys to other hunting grounds. But our funding was specifically for this area. We needed them to stay in one place so we could confront them and hold them accountable. What we really needed was a game-changer.

I organized a meeting up through the NYPD channels and then drove down to One Police Plaza on my way up the building to meet with the highest level of leadership in the department to discuss my idea, which was this: We wanted to wear NYPD jackets and NYPD-shaped badges when conducting our operations. This would send a message that the feds were no longer around.

The leadership pondered it. In the end, to keep everything legal, they agreed and allowed us to wear the jackets but not their badges. Instead, I had new badges created. They looked exactly like the NYPD badges but contained our agency's name. They said Special Agent in tiny lettering instead of a detective. "Not a thing on the badge, said New York Police Department." It was a perfect disguise, and we pinned them upside down on our vests to make it harder for the bad guys to read from a distance.

We blended in perfectly with our NYPD counterparts, and our team worked cohesively. We were a tight group.

One day, while getting ready to deploy and go back out there for a night raid. NYPD Housing Police Officer Gerard Carter (who had been a member of our original team) was in full uniform, sitting inside his patrol van. Next to him was his partner, Eric Storch. On this day, they were cruising outside the West Brighton houses about to serve a warrant. The West Brighton houses were just one of the developments that were part of our case.

Seventeen-year-old Shatiek Johnson was also there. He was already a convicted felon and on parole for beating a homeless man to death over ten bucks. That happened when he was just fifteen.

As Officer Carter spotted Johnson, he did a U-turn because Johnson was wanted for another murder of a twenty-year-old man who was shot fifteen times in the head. And Johnson just happened to be one of the leading drug dealers in our case.

When Johnson spotted the patrol van, he was in its headlights. This seventeen-year-old raised his weapon and shot through the windshield, sending a bullet just above the left eye and into Officer Carter's head as he ducked the shot.

Seconds after the bullet left Johnson's gun, police radios went crazy. Officer Storch, who was right there, was uninjured. He identified the killer and called it in.

NYPD units fanned out to catch the killer. But he was fast and got away.

A task force set up a large-scale manhunt, shutting down the Verrazano Bridge and forming a circle perimeter. Helicopters filled the sky. Armored tanks hit the streets. Several hundred helmeted cops searched everything everywhere.

The killer was smart. He had ducked into a nearby apartment, minimizing his exposure. But NYPD caught him within ten hours of the shooting.

People who know I'm a law enforcement officer would often ask me about the cause of crime. I tell them the story of Shatiek Johnson.

I think we can all agree that kid didn't come out of the womb with a 9mm in his hand. At his trial, I learned more about Mr. Johnson.

First, his father was a drug dealer. Unfortunately, and sadly, he followed in his father's footsteps.

His mother had five sons and had trouble controlling them without a father in their life. A boy needs a father. When he doesn't have one, he'll go out and get one. Mr. Johnson did just that. The gangs and drug dealers offered to be his dad, showing him how to be a man. They explained life's rules to him.

If you thought his older brothers might look after him, the oldest was a drug dealer. Another brother engaged in an out-of-control gunfight. So, the odds were stacked against Johnson.

That doesn't mean we all aren't responsible for our own conduct. We are. But imagine growing up in a world of human feces smeared on the elevator buttons and seeing it's okay to drop a bathroom sink on officers who are risking their lives trying to provide you with a safe place to live.

Many times, I felt like a man standing on the beach with a piece of plywood, trying to hold back the incoming tide. I look to the left and right and see a few of my colleagues scattered down the beach, each holding a piece of plywood. That's what it was like.

So, twenty-eight-year-old Officer Carter is sadly deceased, leaving behind his wife Jozette and his six-year-old son Louis. And Shatiek Johnson is in prison, eligible for parole in 2023 after serving just twenty-five years. Where is the justice in any of that?

Unfortunately, That's the level of violence we dealt with when working on those cases.

To this day, I have a team photo on my wall of fifty incredibly dedicated police officers and myself. Officer Carter stands just a few feet away from me. That picture still sends shivers up my spine.

Officer Gerard Carter. His shift ended on July 31, 1998.

God bless him and his family.

His photo will always be on my wall.

Chapter 11

"Deep Undercover"

Working in New York City brings diversity to the assignments. Not only are there so many different cultures living so close together, but there are all kinds of unique communities, each with its own special personality. Staten Island was one such community.

Wedged between New York and New Jersey, Staten Island is an actual island. It was the last piece of land you saw before passing into the Lower Bay and out to sea.

Unfortunately, at the time, unseen pockets of Staten Island had their share of crime, and drugs.

During a long stretch, I was assigned to a task force aptly named "Ghost Team One". As we wanted to operate in shadows, and a Pontiac GTO was my favorite car.

At the time, we turned out of the nearby undisclosed location. "Turning out" is what police officers do when they start their shift. Essentially, it's roll call and then hitting the streets. The problem arises when you are undercover. You can't come and go at the local precinct station.

152

People you don't want to see will see you and identify you as either a cop or a person working with the cops. Inevitability, you'll get "burnt," meaning you'll blow your cover. Bad guys do their own countersurveillance, and you'll either get spotted or someone will snap a photo and show it to the people you are trying to do business with. Instead, we utilized undisclosed locations we'd establish in advance that were safe locations to meet.

This particular week as part of our "Operation Safe Home" mission, we met in advance at one of our undisclosed locations to plan the execution of a search warrant on a known drug location. It involved a rundown old house on the island. After making controlled buys from the occupants, we had a warrant to search the house. I put on my gear and prepared to "hit' the house with my NYPD counterparts.

As we were getting ready to roll, I looked around at the officers working in the task force office. Everyone was "gearing up."

The plan of attack for this particular raid was from the rear. Everyone thinks we usually bust down the front door like in the movies. Really, that's our last option in some instances. In a great number of cases, the front door is usually rigged with a nasty surprise for the cops. So, we play it safe and always look for the safest method of entry.

To ensure our safety, we had approximately ten detectives and two agents combined on this operation. This included me and my partner, Keaton Coney. He was a tall Irishman who had been around forever. Keaton was solid and the best partner anyone could ask for.

Keaton and I were on the initial team to go in. Our job was to approach from the back of the house, which consisted of negotiating a fence. We needed to clear the fence and gain entry through the rear door once the team in front knocked on the door and announced our presence.

As we crept closer to the fence, we received the word to go. Keaton went first.

"Oh shit!" I heard him say once he was over the fence and out of my sight.

I had my gun out.

"What is it?" I said through the fence.

"There's dog shit everywhere." Funny as it seems, this was a common trick. Drug dealers don't pick up dog poop to keep people from doing exactly what we were attempting. It was a gift for the cops.

"And there's a pit bull coming my way," he said. That was another trick (or treat, depending on which point of view you look at it from).

Drug dealers always had aggressive dogs on their property.

For this operation and our safety, pit bulls constituted bad news. Not only would we have to deal with the dog, but if we had to dispatch the dog, the noise would give away our position. And standing in the backyard trying to dodge dog poop made us sitting ducks. A few seconds in, and this raid was already turning bad.

I hopped over the fence and joined Keaton. Somehow, he had calmed the dog down with some dog treats he conveniently carried in the front pocket of his bulletproof vest and didn't have to shoot it. That was a miracle, and another innocent life was saved. Dog treats and bacon are a necessity for these jobs.

I looked around and saw our teams on either side of the house trying to pry the windows up. That was a non-starter because they were nailed shut and had other security devices. Another dealer tactic was to nail windows shut so no one could break in.

By now, the bad guys had to know we were out there. At any moment, the bullets could start flying.

I ran to the back door and looked through the window. On a table aiming toward the front door was a machine gun. I could see a string attached to the doorknob, which was rigged to a pulley system. So, when the door was opened, it would trigger the machine gun and fire at the incoming officers. I grabbed the radio and screamed, "Don't go near the front door! It's a trap!"

The team in front got the word just in time and held off. Keaton and I busted in with a handful of other officers working on the house's sides. Keaton removed the string off the doorknob and let everybody in. It was a close one.

"What the hell?" I heard Keaton say.

It was at that moment; I spun around and saw a Saint Bernard stagger toward us. He leaned at a sharp angle, about to fall down. It didn't take long to see this place was a cookhouse. The stench was terrible. The dog had been breathing drug fumes for so long that he was messed up and apparently had a stroke.

I'm sure some folks out there might wonder why we didn't know about the dog in the backyard or the poop. Or even that there was a machine gun pointed at the front door. The answer is due to several factors.

First, the low-level dealers we had purchased the drugs from identified this house for us. We had not been making controlled buys from the occupants. They were the distributors. Instead, we'd watched dealers come and go. Then, we obtained a warrant based on our observations and the information from the dealers we had cut deals with. Thus, we had never even been to the front door.

Next, sending an agent to the back fence and peeking over is too dangerous. It's a great way to get shot or at least cause the dealers to move elsewhere. And believe me, they will.

Finally, there's the time factor. When we receive information on a house, we have to hurry. Lives are in danger due to the drugs being sold. We don't have weeks to scope out every part of the house. And we don't have the money to pay the detectives to do that. We have so many places selling drugs that we take the most reasonable precautions we can, working with the budget we're given. That's how it is. Even the federal government's bank account has a bottom.

After checking out the downstairs and finding no one, I walked into the kitchen and noticed the refrigerator door open. The smell was horrific. Molding food at least a year old sat rotting on every shelf. I won't ever get that smell out of my nostrils.

Encountering rotten odors is part of the job too. That's why many of us carried DOA crystals. DOA means Dead On Arrival. The coroner's office uses these crystals when dealing with decomposing bodies. Once inside, a few officers used a Kelly tool to pry open some windows. I set the crystals on the ledges to help clear the place out. I always carried them with me.

The other officers had run upstairs ahead of us. Keaton and I followed them and found a woman in the hallway, stoned, with most of her hair gone. An older woman in a bedroom was also stoned. She turned out to be the mother of the first woman.

I walked into the middle bedroom and found a seventeen-year-old boy. He was the son of the woman who was missing her hair. And he was high too.

On the other side of him was a closed-off room.

"I think someone is behind the door," Keaton whispered.

"I'm going through the ceiling."

We gave him a boost up to the attic access hole in the hall and waited as he crawled over to the room to see who was in there. Suddenly, we heard a loud crash and Keaton moaning.

Another detective and I kicked in the door to find Keaton with his legs dangling through the ceiling. At least the room was empty.

We put on our masks because the air was so thick with drugs and chemicals. Then, we tried to sort everything out.

First, there were baggies, vials, and cooking tools everywhere. We pulled out our evidence bags and began collecting them.

During a thorough search of the place, we collected a large amount of crack and crystal meth. This would take a lot of time for someone.

It was clear the drug dealers weren't there. Whether or not they'd been tipped off, we never found out. But they had enslaved and addicted the people who lived in this house so they could use the place to cook drugs. This is a common tactic since they don't like owning real estate or paying property taxes. And it's easy to pick up stakes and move to another house. Yet the damage they leave behind is immense.

In the boy's room, we found an exotic bird—a $3,000 Macaw—that was just as messed up as the Saint Bernard. Half its feathers were gone, and it apparently suffered a stroke. It was unfortunate.

"Hey, take a look at this," a newer detective told me.

I walked over to find him staring at the wall. "What do you have?"

"Look at the walls," he said.

"They're moving."

"Get used to it," I told him.

"In these cookhouses, a waxy yellow substance cakes up on the walls. The cockroaches come out to eat it. That's why it looks like the walls are moving."

"There must be millions of them," he said, both fascinated and grossed out at the same time.

"Probably. And all of them are addicts."

He shook his head in disgust, walking away.

"What the f...?" an NYPD cop yelled.

Keaton and I went to see what the problem was this time.

"Take a look at this," the cop said, pointing to the wall.

Keaton and I moved closer.

There were at least fifty Polaroid photos pinned to the wall. Each one showed acts of incest between the seventeen-year-old boy and his mother, the one missing her hair. It was horrific and tremendously sad.

I blinked several times and walked around, taking in the carnage. None of the mattresses had sheets. Every living creature in the house was high. It was as close to hell as anyone wanted to get. I kept thinking no one would ever believe me if I told them. Outside, people go about their daily lives driving past this location without a clue to what's actually going on in this house of horrors.

The mother and grandmother were arrested for outstanding warrants. The mother was investigated for sexually assaulting her son. And the boy was put in rehab. We didn't catch the high-level drug dealers that day but continued to pursue them. All we had to deal with was the mess they left behind for society to clean up.

When I hear people talk about how drugs are not dangerous and don't harm anyone, I think about raids like that. Until you see the horrors I've seen, you just don't know. Drugs have massive consequences. In this case, three generations were affected.

***

I loved undercover work. But maintaining my UC cover took a lot of effort and a lot of time. To realistically pose as a contractor, I spent time shopping at Salvation Army and Goodwill stores. I needed clothes that were heavily used. And then I rarely washed them.

To make the pants look real, I pulled out the hems and either stapled them back or duct-taped them. I bought extremely worn boots with paint all over them. My best pair of boots set me back one dollar. Some of my good friends from NYPD who worked undercover assignments helped me out with extra worn uniforms they had left over.

My body had to match the clothes. To accomplish this, I grew a mini–ZZ Top style goatee and shaved my head. Sometimes, I didn't shave for five days. On occasion, I'd go for days without showering. This produced a good cloud of sweat stink that surrounded me. Trust me, it kept certain people away while adding to my credibility.

No one ever thinks an undercover would go to such lengths, but it's what makes you the best at your craft. Study the environment and become the environment. Hide in plain sight. By working hard, I'm proud to say my cover was never burned in my five years of undercover work.

To keep my undercover vehicle in character, I had to buy fast food and eat half of it, leaving the leftovers and wrappers on the dashboard. I added four Police Benevolence Association stickers to the front windshield that people buy to help keep them from getting tickets. I even snagged a local Union sticker and slapped that on the vehicle. The last thing I needed was a union hassle when blending in on a job site.

The long hours it took to maintain my cover were nothing compared to the time it took to arrange a set. For everyone's safety, it was vital to have the staging of a set well-thought-out. If not, your movie would involve scenes of cops getting hurt or shot. And I'd never ever jeopardize anyone's safety.

Take your time to check all the boxes. Do it right because everyone has a family, and everyone wants to go home at the end of the day.

When I was the director of a set, I spent days walking around it. I'd eat a burger in a restaurant. Then I'd go into a shop. If they had liquor stores, I would visit one and buy something. I never looked out of place. I lived the set. I lived in it.

Once I had a good feel for the environment, we'd go to stage two. This involved placing ghosts on the set. Ghosts are undercover cops who are there for safety backup. They also watch what's happening and alert the director if something bad is happening.

To insert a ghost properly, they might get off a bus and head to a deli for a sandwich. The ghost would pick a seat that looks out on the set. After eating, the ghost might smoke a cigarette outside. Many times, my ghosts were homeless people. Since the sets were in rough areas, they fit right in.

The bottom line with directors, ghosts, and anyone stepping on the set was that we didn't just pull up in a car to get into position. We had to slide our actors into place. This took hours because we were up against smart and observant criminals. They had kids always looking for stuff out of place, people who didn't belong there. We would have ghosts start moving on and off the set two weeks in advance for important investigations.

Once the set was just right, we could have the Uncles (or UCs) come onto the set. Again, they had been easing into the area for hours. Only after all this work would we have the Uncles make controlled buys.

Hours, days, and weeks were the price we paid to catch big fish. That's why I was stunned during my first year at the Inspector General when my boss pulled me into her office and gave me the news.

"Congratulations, Tony. The FBI needs help on a big investigation. Here's the phone number for the case agent. Call him and get going."

By this time, I knew the FBI was mandated to partner with us whenever we had public corruption cases. When I called the case agent and found out what this was about, they wanted me to be the Technical Surveillance Agent for the case. My job was to get everything on audio and video to support a successful prosecution. This was an investigation that, if I did it right, would boost my credibility as a "Tech Agent" in the investigative circles around New York and New Jersey.

HUD had given millions of dollars to the third-largest city in New Jersey—the City of Paterson. The money was supposed to be used to fix potholes and sidewalks, among other issues. Instead, it had gone to friends and relatives of the mayor, who happened to be low bidders. There were other irregularities, so HUD opened an investigation. In a few short days, the FBI was brought in. Now, suddenly, I was brought in.

I went to the safe house where the investigation was being handled and met the case leaders.

They pulled me into a room.

"I need you to wire a guy up."

"Okay," I said.

"My schedule is free all day on Thursday and half on Friday."

"What?" he said with an incredulous expression.

"Half on Friday," I told him. "The morning half."

He smirked. "Don't worry about Thursday or Friday. We're doing it now."

"Now?!" I replied. "I need days to get ready, I have system."

"I'm sorry, but you're here, and you are all we have. The informant will be here in twenty minutes. You have that much time to prepare."

"When are you sending him out?" I asked, finding all this hard to believe.

"Forty minutes."

That's how fast this investigation moved. When people discover there's, a federal investigation happening, if they're worried about their involvement, they must make a quick calculation. Am I going to get caught or not? If the answer is yes, they must decide if cooperation is possible.

The feds need only a few cooperating witnesses.

Once the chairs are taken, and the music stops, the people still standing must face a jury. That means exoneration or decades behind bars. It's an easy choice for most people to cooperate—if they get there fast enough.

Seemingly overnight, we wired the City of Paterson for video and sound. Cars. Diners. Motel rooms. You name it. The entire town was bugged.

I set up several OPs and LPs (Observation and Listening Posts). This allowed me to capture signals from several transmitters.

My best move was driving my surveillance vehicle to the top of a parking garage and setting up an OP (Observation Post) there. With my boss, the Special Agent in Charge, sitting in the back with me, it was somewhat intimidating. I had to get it right.

To capture moving conversations, I had several directional antennae. At the same time, I had to guess where the subjects might go at any moment. I also had UC agents on the street with recording equipment. They weren't technical electronics surveillance agents, but they learned quickly and did the job.

There I was from the top of the garage, conducting the orchestra. I had to laugh because every other investigation after this one would be a piece of cake.

After months of investigation, Mayor Barnes was indicted by Chris Christie. Mayor Barnes vowed to fight the charges. He also ran for a second term, losing badly to Mayor Jose "Joey" Torres. After that loss, the wind seemed to disappear from his sails. Mayor Barnes eventually pled guilty and received a thirty-seven-month sentence.

As for Mayor Jose "Joey" Torres, he was very popular. He went on to three terms before being convicted of using city workers for personal work. He was sentenced to five years and did a little more than one year in the New Jersey prison system.

And as for the City of Paterson, there must be something in the water.

***

Drug deals happen everywhere. You could pick any city block, and you'd learn where to buy drugs within a few days. You could make some buys and bust them by the end of the week.

East Orange, New Jersey, was a place of focus for HUD. During a hot summer, I was assigned there to do some buy-busts in the federally subsidized housing developments. A buy-bust is where a UC buys the drugs and makes the bust immediately.

Buy-busts have their advantages.

First, you don't have to track the guy down later when you want to arrest him. Next, after he's finished soiling his britches, you can cut a deal with him to roll upward on his supplier. If you do this day in and day out, you can move up several levels and wreak havoc on the local drug trade.

It was a hot evening when I parked my surveillance vehicle in East Orange. In the back with me was a detective from the East Orange Police Department. As usual, I laid out my entire spread from Little Italy.

The detective and I were chowing down, sitting there watching the TV screens waiting for the buy-bust to happen. It was hot outside for the UC agents but nice and cool inside the van. We were having so much fun that the detective turned to me and said, "I've got to do this detail with you from now on, Secret Squirrel." Secret Squirrel is short cop slang for a government agent. Street cops liked to call us "Squirrels."

We were cutting into the lasagna when we heard a call on the radio. The undercover car sitting a half-mile away peeled off and left. That was our "cover car" in case something happened to us or the unit. But we weren't worried because the odds of something happening to us were low, at least we'd thought.

As an added precaution, there were cameras installed inside and all around the outside of my surveillance vehicle. Specific security cameras weren't there to watch the action but for the security of the unit we were in. Several were on the roof, and I'd also put cameras in the front and back of the vehicle. But I needed one more.

The cab where I sat when driving was separated from the back compartment by a thin wall. An opening at the bottom allowed me to crawl to the back. Once back there, I slid the door closed, and no one knew I was still there.

Unfortunately, that left the cab uncovered by cameras. To fix this, I took a construction hardhat and installed a fisheye lens. Hung it on a hook in the front cab. Now, I have a 180-degree picture of the cab and the windows. Everything was covered inside and out.

Ten minutes after we lost our cover car, a suspicious vehicle rolled alongside us. During our enjoyment of the Italian buffet, the detective informed me that a car was stolen every five minutes in East Orange. Seeing this car creep up slowly alerted both of us.

We finished chewing our food and set down our plates. The driver of the suspicious car was coming toward our vehicle.

Quickly and quietly, I grabbed my government-issued shotgun that was resting on the floor at my feet. The suspect tried the door handles on the driver's side, then the passenger's side. Next, he tried the handle on the sliding door. Since it was all locked, he was out of luck. But a guy like this was used to making his own luck.

We watched on the cameras as he pulled out a lockpick set. The detective jumped on the radio and whispered, "We need backup now; a stolen car suspect is attempting to steal the unit we're in!"

Dispatch said a patrol car was on the way. But we couldn't tell how long it would take, so we figured they probably weren't going to make it.

The thief started working on the passenger door. Any second, he'd have it open. When he did, I knew I'd have to confront him. We were too close to risk him pulling a gun and seeing if he could shoot through the thin panel in the cab or even the skin of the van. And, of course, the whole operation would be at risk.

The detective pointed to the sliding door panel. He was going to pull it back, and I would stick the gun out. If that didn't scare the thief off, I'd have to take more direct action.

"I'll count to three," he whispered. "On zero, I'll pull it open, and you go to work."

Gripping the shotgun, I nodded and held my weapon steady.

"Three...two...one..."

Chapter 12

"Capture the enemy flag!"

I swallowed hard when I heard him say, "Zero."

The East Orange detective pulled the door back a few inches. I shoved the shotgun barrel out. He was so intent on "picking" the lock that he didn't hear us.

Suddenly, he dropped the pick. Little did he know I had my finger on the trigger guard, prepared for the worst-case scenario: him entering my van with a weapon. Just over my shoulder was the detective, his weapon drawn. Yet the suspect retrieved his pick and continued working, oblivious to us.

Just as he was about to open the passenger door, our original cover car rolled up, and two officers got out. The suspect caught a glimpse of them and immediately withdrew, shoving the pick in his pocket. Then, he started walking casually down the sidewalk.

When the officers approached him, he played it cool. And why not? They couldn't have seen what he was doing. Meanwhile, we were on the radio telling the officers we had him on video trying to break in. They made the arrest. Months later, the suspect pleaded guilty after his lawyer saw the video. At least he's still alive to steal another car.

***

Events like that were common in East Orange. I'd see criminal activity often but couldn't break cover. If I did, lives would be at risk, and money would disappear down the drain. Instead, I'd have to call it in and let the local Police handle it.

One such situation happened when I was parked at a public housing development in Queens. We were looking for drug deals occurring in a particular apartment. I had rigged the apartment with a remote camera system, so we had it completely cased.

We had undercover officers bringing people over to buy drugs. My job was to sit in the van in the parking lot and monitor the cameras.

It was 5 p.m., another great day on the job. The normally busy parking lot was quiet. I had a detective with me. This time, we had a beautiful Vietnamese buffet laid out. The detective bit into a fresh gỏi cuốn while I sat there shoveling in some bánh cuốn. Suddenly, a car pulled into the open spot next to the van.

We studied the car, waiting for the driver to get out. But he never did. Instead, he slid over to the passenger seat and started getting his groove on with a woman. This lasted some time until the matter concluded.

It was clear he had picked up this woman from a few streets over. She was a prostitute. Since experienced prostitutes already had the money in hand before they exchanged services, they didn't need to have any more interaction. Yet he began demanding his money

169

back. Scared to death, she produced it, along with her day's haul. As I said before, this is called a rip.

We called it in, but the car pulled away, presumably to drop her off so she could start all over again. It was a terrible way to make a living.

After I turned over the tapes, NYPD tried to find the suspect. We studied his t-shirt and lifted the name of a company. It was a local construction outfit. Detectives went there, but nobody matched the suspect's description. Sadly, we were never able to locate him. And the prostitute, who was interviewed but not arrested, refused to file charges. Who knows what that criminal is doing today?

***

I had one undercover assignment that had it all. It was an apartment in Yonkers. The tenant had stated on his Section 8 application that he was broke and unemployed. Yet at 10 p.m., he left the apartment and went to work. They had a detective in a car ready to follow him. I was called in because they needed my help getting him on video, leaving the apartment, closing the front door, and getting into his car. That's the level of resources the government spends to stop fraud.

My cover on this case was as an electrician. So, I tried to find a few creative places just outside his front door to place a camera. It was just too risky, and it was very dark. This would be a tough one.

To solve the problem, I drove the van to a parking spot close to the apartment. Then I tossed infrared glow sticks in the bushes near the front door. The naked eye can't detect them. But on my high-dollar camera in the van, it was Giants Stadium during a night game. Still, I'd have to be good and quick with the camera to get a solid facial recognition that would hold up in court. For court, it takes a person's image, the approximate size of a thumbprint, to be discernable.

While I sat there waiting for him to leave his apartment, the same glow sticks lit up the parking lot and surrounding area. I saw people having sex in a car. The things I see when conducting surveillance in parking lots. A few spots over, three drug dealers sat on the end of their car doing drugs. And right in front of me, a guy smashed a window and stole a car. It's always tough when this happens because I can't break cover unless it's a life-or-death situation. I'd just call it in and let the cops handle the matter.

I often wondered if we just took my surveillance vehicle and parked it from 4 p.m. until 4 a.m., how many crimes would we catch? Just have a guy sit there and film everything. Even private companies could do this. One guy in a high-tech surveillance platform would stop a ton of crime.

Of course, I snagged the man's face, and it held up in court. Another fraud was eliminated. (Although I often wondered what the housing development's landscapers thought about finding all those glow sticks in the bushes.)

***

Working as a "Narco Ranger," I learned there were two interesting aspects of drug buys and busts: runners and cash. First, I want to tell you about running.

On most operations, twenty of us would roll up in vans and jump out, all yelling, "Police! Get your hands up!"

The bad guys, mostly young adults, would scatter in twenty different directions. They were light and fast, all wearing high-quality basketball shoes.

We, on the other hand, wore high-top boots to protect us from the glass vials, needles, and feces scattered everywhere. Having learned to lighten my boots in the Border Patrol, I was faster than my colleagues. Yet these kids could easily outrun me. I was nicknamed "Conejo," or rabbit in Spanish, in the Border Patrol because I was so fast.

Over time, I calculated that I had caught one out of three suspects I chased. And my catch rate was high. I was like a wild African lion, the kind you see on TV. If I didn't catch a gazelle in the first 200 feet, the gazelle would be gone.

The other part of chasing runners was knowledge. These dealers knew the place better than anyone. They could lead you down an alley where someone was waiting to clobber you or, worse, shoot you in the face. It was highly dangerous.

Now, the cash part. I quickly learned cash was a big necessity. Drug dealers don't take checks, and they don't take American Express.

I was given an ATM card for official use on specific case investigations to ensure we had plenty of cash on hand. Anytime I needed it, I could withdraw funds to support my cases. Of course, I had to account for every penny I spent and stay within the operation's assigned budget. Needless to say, it also came with a good chunk of paperwork as well. There were always auditors checking my numbers and receipts.

Most of my investigations were huge. HUD would designate $1 million or more to combat guns, gangs, and drugs in a particular federally subsidized housing development. That budget would cover my time, overtime for local Police, "buy money" as it's sometimes referred to, "weed and seed" money, equipment, safehouses, administrative supplies, and overtime for any fellow enforcement officers working on the case. But in reality, we lacked the manpower. There were only so many drugs we could buy and doors we could kick down in a day. It's like sending me into the forest and demanding I catch every ant. It ain't gonna happen. So, what do you do when you have the money but lack the men?

You pick up the phone and call for help.

The New York HUD's go-to agency was the NYPD. Sure, we brought in the smaller police departments if necessary. But NYPD had the manpower and the hardware. We would pay them for their hours, including overtime. Essentially, HUD supplemented their payroll when they worked on our cases. This helped them, or any police agency we worked with, tremendously while giving their younger cops valuable experience. It was a great symbiotic relationship.

The great part of working with other agencies was the people you met. Some of them were memorable. One character that I fully enjoyed was Captain Parks of the NYPD. He was a Marine Corps veteran of the Vietnam War. And he was big on capturing the "enemy's flag," as he called it.

I once went to his office and saw the huge collection of flags from Vietnam. He was almost out of the room with the ones he'd added from doing previous drug raids.

I never realized it much until I started working with Capt. Parks, but many of the drug dealers had their country's flag pinned to a wall. On every raid, he'd yell, "Capture the enemy flag!" He was crazy about getting that gang's flag.

With one specific million-dollar investigation I was assigned, we were charged with cleaning up another Staten Island housing development. There are two possible strategies for each operation. Strategy A was to target a suspect or specific set of dealers. This was like a sniper's approach. It took a lot of time, planning, and thought.

Other times, we went with Strategy B. That involved little thought and planning. Instead, we would make controlled buys every day, rain, or shine. We would arrest their dealers a few days later and try to roll them up to the next level. In this Staten Island investigation, we were executing Strategy B.

One day, we were planning to raid a drug source we had rolled up to. Capt. Parks and NYPD would be on this mission.

That morning, I showed up for work at the local Peanut distribution warehouse. HUD had a lease agreement with the company for undercovers to work there. Like the armory, it provided us with a cover.

As I walked into the office, there was Capt. Parks, holding my chair. Before I could say a word, he was on me.

"Where's my check, Secret Squirrel?

You ain't sitting down until I get my check; that's an NYPD-funded chair. When I get my check, then you can sit down." He jerked the chair away.

"Come on Cap," I said.

"Really, Cap, I can't sit down?"

"Nope, tell me, how many enemy flags have you captured?" he barked.

"I've got plenty of flags," I replied.

"From where?"

"When I played football. But they were all yellow." I smiled at him.

That was the type of conversation we had.

Being an Inspector General Special Agent, I was always going on dangerous raids, and so were the NYPD cops; they were used to that kind of daily action. They were always looking to make their bones so they could be promoted. They loved the work.

I wanted to be the first through the door. Capt. Parks convinced me to hang back and let the younger guys bust down the door. After thinking about it, I agreed.

On this day, we had a team ready to raid a house where some midlevel dealers operated. We anticipated a big haul, so the media was coming along.

We arrived at the building, jumped out of the van, and ran. Capt. Parks was right next to me, a banged-up hammerless .32 caliber in his holster he'd been carrying for 20-plus years.

For cops, a .32 was an old gun. No one in law enforcement carried one because they were limited to six rounds and lacked the stopping power. But he had to have one. It was an old-school tradition of sorts, like swivel holsters back in the day.

After we knocked and announced, the apartment door flew open. Two of our men went in. Right behind them was Capt. Parks and me.

The plan was for him to run right and me to run left. But before we could separate, he yelled, "Capture the enemy flag."

I looked ahead and saw a Dominican Republic flag on the back wall. I was about to ignore him when a dealer in the living room jumped up from behind a couch and ran to the window.

Capt. Parks yelled, "I'll get him!"

I had to laugh. There was no way he could fit through the window, and certainly no way he could run this guy down.

Regardless, we both spun on our heels and dashed out the front door. Sure enough, we spotted the guy running. And he had a good lead on us. Too good. This gazelle would probably get away.

With his bulletproof vest looking a little like a lobster bib over his gut, Capt. Parks pumped his arms hard. Again, I laughed inside because I'd learned to run in the Border Patrol. This guy was doing it all wrong… until he passed me. Somehow, he shifted into fifth gear. I couldn't believe it; hey, former Marine, what can I say. Still, there was no way he could bag this suspect. He was too far gone.

Somehow, I focused, pushing myself to catch up to Parks. I was just about to draw even with him when he shifted into sixth gear or had a burst of nitro. As he flew like the wind, a ballcap on his head blew past me. This left a five-foot strip of hair trailing behind him. It looked like a banner those planes fly over stadiums. I tried to read the message in his hair, but there wasn't one.

Before I knew it, he was on top of the guy, maintaining an overwatch. "Get on this guy, Squirrel!" he yelled at me while he waved that .32 around with one hand and tried to reassemble his hair banner with the other.

I took over and cuffed him. As I caught my breath, I gazed up at the old man who'd beaten me to the gazelle. Who would've guessed old Capt. Parks still had some giddy-up?

The media ran behind us to get some photos. Instead of putting his gun away, Capt. Parks continued using both hands to swirl his hair into a circle on top. But at least he wasn't bald like me. At least I faced the music years ago, shaved my head completely, and looked like a WWE Wrestler. Hey, it was a good look. I looked like Stone-Cold Steve Austin; not a bad choice at all.

Of course, we made a haul: drugs, guns, and stolen radios. After things calmed down and I looked over the weapons, I realized this could have gone the other way. The guns were ready to fire. There were a ton of them.

We nabbed all five dealers in the house, so the media made it look good. And several NYPD officers made their bones. That meant they put a top case on their work resume for promotion purposes. It was time to celebrate.

After a successful raid like that, we usually retired to the Embers Restaurant on Third Ave. in Bay Ridge, Brooklyn. It overlooked the Verrazzano-Narrows Bridge. The place had a special charm.

Its dark wooden floors and tables were lit by candles and a few wall sconces. A doorway had been cut into the main wall, giving the staff access to Vinnie's Meat Market, a butcher shop that opened in

1954. They sold meat to the public and provided whatever you ordered to the restaurant's kitchen. It was a great place.

At the time, Lou Rocanelli owned and ran both the meat market and the restaurant. Lou was the ultimate character. He stood about four-foot-one-inch in his sharkskin suit. With a perfectly pressed clip-on tie and a ring on his pinky, he lorded over the joint.

When I was going there, Lou was married but going through a divorce. The woman hanging on his arm looked like Loni Anderson, towering above him. Just looking at him, you would have thought he was "mobbed up."

I'll always remember my first time in Embers. I walked in and started looking for a table. That was a big no-no. You don't sit down until Lou seats you. There are two reasons for that. First, the place is small. He can't afford to have you sit there and not spend much money. The second reason is etiquette. The left side of the restaurant is for cops, and the right side is for, well, you know, the other guys—the *wise* guys.

"Can I help you?" he asked, looking me over.

I told him I was meeting Keaton Coney, my colleague.

"Then you need to sit at the bar."

I looked at the small bar. "Okay," I replied, not willing to argue with him.

"And you need to order a drink," he said gruffly.

"I can't afford to have people in here not spending money. I have to make each seat count."

I ordered a two-dollar drink that cost me twelve dollars and looked around. For sure, he didn't have many tables. In New York City, every square inch counts.

Keaton eventually showed up, and we had a brilliant meal. As I left and Lou scanned my credit card receipt, he let me know I was welcome to come back. That was music to my ears because I was hooked.

Over the years, many of the Narco Rangers met to celebrate successful raids. Not so much that we bagged many drugs, bad guys, or weapons. It was mostly to celebrate the fact that we were still alive. Embers was a place to enjoy *because* you were alive. We breathed in the ambiance as we inhaled the steaks.

One day, I went in, and Lou sat me at my special table. I was greeted by my favorite waiter, Donny. He handed me a menu and gave me the bad news. "Hey, Tony, this is my last day to serve you."

"What happened?" I asked.

"You're giving all this up?"

"No, I sold my spot."

"You sold your spot?" I asked.

Donny told me he was a union waiter. I knew a little about union waiters. They were very professional, wiping the crumbs in front of you and carrying over platters of raw meat from the butcher's shop for you to pick out your piece. Union waiters provided great service.

I learned that the union had put Donny in this place fifteen years ago when he'd purchased his spot (essentially, he bought his position and his job, like you purchase a franchise.) He earned a salary from the restaurant and all the tips he could snag. He made a nice living. But recently, he sold his spot for $60,000.

I asked Keaton about it and learned the restaurant owner doesn't own that position. It worked out initially with the waiter's union when they first opened up. It's like a Taxicab medallion or fast-food franchise. If the restaurant closes, the waiter is screwed. But the union will place him somewhere else. They usually take care of him.

Donny said he'd sold his position to a young man. That guy will work for 20 years, and that'll be his career. And then, he might sell it or give it to his son if Embers is still there. As of now, it's closed for good. Sad to see an institution like that closed; I spent many evenings there. Cops on one side and wise guys on the other. It was neutral ground. There was an unwritten ceasefire. A time for all of us to take a break and break bread civilly.

Embers turned out to be an experience like no other. I hope it lasts forever!

***

One frustrating aspect of working narcotics enforcement was the bugs. Moving around these drug houses stirred up every insect imaginable. They were hungry for fresh meat, and I often provided the meal.

Coming home, my clothes would be full of lice, fleas, and anything else that crawled. Usually, I would change at the station, placing my clothes in plastic bags to kill some of them. Later, it took a healthy dose of hot water to eliminate the rest. Hopefully.

On some investigations, I wasn't close to the station when I finished for the day. Instead, I came directly home to my midtown Manhattan five-story walk-up apartment. I would stand in the hallway, hearing my girlfriend say, "Take off your clothes right now! You're not coming in here wearing that."

I knew she was right. Bringing in lice, roaches, and whatever else was stupid. To keep the peace, I undressed in the hallway.

Speaking of my apartment, it was only 450 square feet. The place was so small that you had to go outside if you wanted to do a jumping jack. Literally, the apartment was so small to change your mind; you had to go to the roof.

Rent was controlled at $775 a month, the best she and I could afford, especially since cops and special agents don't make a lot of money. Again, the big reward is the "retirement"—that is if you're still alive to collect it.

My girlfriend, Amy, and I had been dating for some time. Eventually, I figured she'd put up with me long enough. I had to do something special.

At the time, Amy worked for the state of New York as a Worker's Compensation Senior Fraud Investigator. Before this, she'd had a varied career.

Amy was an actress in soap operas. She played the hotel manager in one series. Amy was also cast in several off-Broadway plays. At one point, she was the face of the Lifetime Channel. They showed her face every time they ran a short ad for the Lifetime Channel.

Amy had also been a model at the Ford Modeling Agency. Finally, she'd been one of the managers at Caroline's Comedy Club in Times Square. If there was ever a woman who understood what I had been through in life, it was her.

One day, I went shopping on the street and bought her a set of pearls for $150 from the jewelry brokers on Diamond Way in New York City. Sadly, I didn't have enough money to buy a ring at the time, or at least one that wouldn't rust.

I ordered dinner and picked it up, sneaking it up to a picnic table on the roof of the building, or "Tar Beach," as New Yorkers affectionally call the roof of their apartment building. There really aren't any backyards in New York City, so your roof becomes your backyard and your beach.

With everything set, I collected Amy and took her to Tar Beach. We ate dinner and watched the skyscrapers and the lights of Times Square just three blocks away. It was absolutely amazing.

Once dinner was over, I dropped to one knee and proposed. I was truly blessed when Amy said yes.

For our wedding, we played James Taylor's *Up On a Roof.* And for my wedding night, once again, I stood at the entrance to our hotel suite and heard her say, "Take off your clothes right now!

You're not coming in here wearing that."

Chapter 13

9/11, Responding to the attacks

Driving around in an electrician's van with a shaved head and fake tattoos, I never knew what might happen. One day, I received a call that I was urgently needed in Manhattan to wire up a cop. I was next to the West Side Highway, which was the fastest way there. The problem with the West Side Highway is that no commercial vehicles are allowed on it. Period!

True New Yorkers understand toll roads and commercial vehicles go together. It's another way for New York City to grab some additional tax revenue. As such, commercial vehicles would love to travel down non-toll roads. But those are heavily watched by law enforcement. A driver can easily get busted. The fines are heavy. Arrests are possible. It's just not worth it.

This day, though, I had to get to Manhattan fast. I had no choice.

As I entered the highway, I reached over and cranked up the radio, getting into my role as an undercover electrician. I pushed the van to 55 mph to keep up with the heavy traffic. Out of nowhere, an NYPD cruiser pulled up on my driver's side. They always seem to come out of nowhere. Glancing over, I noticed its passenger's side window rolling down when a sergeant stuck his head out.

Keep in mind the lanes are tight on the West Side Highway. That put the sergeant's face real close to mine. I rolled down my window and looked over. Before I could say anything, he yelled, "Really?" Meaning, what the hell are you doing driving a big commercial van down the west side highway.

I smiled and said nothing.

He shook his head and yelled louder. "Are you out of your mind?! You should know better."

Again, I smiled. But this time, I reached down to a hidden panel in the door and pulled out my secret weapon. Casually, I flipped a plaque at the sergeant. It bore the word "Police" in big, bold letters along with another set of letters—NYPD. These plaques were specially produced by the U.S. Customs Agency and approved by NYPD for use in New York City, primarily for parking, but they worked great for identification as well because they were so hard to get.

He pulled his head inside the patrol car and spoke to the driver. They talked for a few seconds before he returned to the window. The sergeant's eyes scanned my truck, starting at the front bumper and slowly moving to the rear. Then, he stared at my ZZ Top goatee. A quick shake of his head in disbelief was followed by a thumbs-up and a smile. His window rolled back up, and the cruiser slipped back into traffic, disappearing for good.

That moment stayed with me. Because it was eerily similar to that dreadful morning on September 11, 2001, when I cruised at top speed down the West Side Highway to downtown Manhattan. Racing to respond to the attacks on the World Trade Center.

Without traffic, I flew like the wind. In fact, I was the only vehicle on the road. Everything else was coming out of the city.

My destination was HUD's main office at 26 Federal Plaza. Dan, my boss, had called me on the Nextel unit, ordering me to get down there immediately. "Bring everything you've got," he had said. "We're gonna need it."

At the end of the highway, I reached a stopping point. Already NYPD established checkpoints. Each one took time for me to clear, but my police plaque and my credentials got me through, despite my appearance and type of vehicle.

I'd just cleared a checkpoint shortly before the North Tower fell. I didn't believe the radio report until I saw a gray-white fog racing down the streets. When dust-covered executives came stumbling toward me, I knew we were at war.

Eventually, I cleared the last checkpoint and parked the van in the middle of the intersection at Duane Street and Broadway, just outside the 26 Federal Plaza building. I tried to get to ground zero, but it was just two crazy and there were clouds of smoke and too much rubble. The dust cloud was still so thick I couldn't see the World Trade Center. My new office was there—at Six World Trade Center. But I knew it was gone.

Stunned at this new reality, I spotted Chris, a uniformed police officer I knew. He was carrying a woman covered in dust and blood. I jumped out and helped carry her to safety. As we set her down in the lobby of 26 Federal Plaza, I could see that she had bloody wounds to her head. The white dust covering her made the blood appear pink. It also covered up some of the wounds. Still, whatever injuries she had, it looked bad. I couldn't see her making it.

No sooner had we released her than we encountered more people needing help. We set up an impromptu rescue crew. Chris and I helped as many people as we could. I directed people to run uptown, away from the Trade Center and the debris. It felt like the end of the world. You could barely see, and people were screaming and running in every direction. Whoever needed help, I helped. A Con Edison worker yelled, Officer, and tossed me a blue Con Edison helmet so I had something for protection. This went on for maybe fifteen to twenty minutes.

I had just set down an injured man when my Nextel rang. It was the boss again.

"Tony! This is really bad. I need you to rally at the office. I need you to…" His voice was cut off.

"Hello?" I said into the flip phone. "Hello? Dan, are you still there?"

Soldiers talk about the fog of war. This was it. Smoke. Debris falling from the sky. Dazed people covered in white soot and blood, walking in every direction, their briefcases stuck to their hands. If I didn't know better, I'd swear they were zombies. That's how horrific this scene was.

When you're faced with an enemy, adversity, or something so unreal you could never imagine happening, you run back to the comfort of your training. Muscle memory, as we call it, in law enforcement. All the months, weeks, and training days had prepared me for such a moment. I placed my hands down by my sides. I concentrated on holding my heart rate steady. My breathing was level. My mind was focused—not scared or panicked. And, believe me, it wouldn't have taken much to slip gears into the panic zone.

I dusted myself off and looked around at the nightmare. A firetruck covered in soot. A sagging awning. Paperwork from filing cabinets that no longer existed floated lazily to earth. Nothing made sense. The end of the world was here.

Through the chaos, more uniformed police officers arrived. They carried injured citizens to the front of 26 Federal Plaza. I continued helping them, hoping to make my way to the office where, supposedly, my boss waited.

For what seemed like hours, people were moved to safety, with many of them screaming for water or help. I had no concept of time until my phone rang again.

"Get up here quick," my boss said. "We're rallying up here right now."

In reality, after moving my van from the intersection to a safer area, I had only been helping for about 20 minutes. But it seemed like an eternity.

After helping a woman sit down, I sprinted inside the main lobby and took the elevator to the 34th floor. The Inspector General had a suite at the end of that floor—space for about twenty employees to work. I found my two bosses, Danny and Sara, waiting in a conference room.

Sara was covered in white soot and bleeding. She had been in Six World Trade Center when the South Tower fell. Our unit had a large suite on the 6th floor of that building. If she had stayed longer, she would've been dead when the North Tower fell into Six World Trade Center, cutting it in half.

"How did you get out of there?" I asked.

"Rode on a firetruck," she replied. I could see she was dazed, so I sat her in a chair.

"What do you want to do, Dan?" I asked.

"The command post was originally at St. Mary's Church, but that didn't last long. It was too close to Ground Zero, and now you couldn't see anything with the plum of ash. When the South Tower fell, they told me it was being moved north to the DEA's office on 10th Avenue. We need to get there because the FBI has told us we're now attached to the Joint Terrorism Task Force."

I went to look out the window. White dust was everywhere. There were black plumes of smoke rising from Ground Zero. Even from the 34th floor, I could hear people screaming.

"Dan," I said, "this is the end of the world. We've got to get back down there and help people.

They're in chaos."

"No, Tony," he said sternly.

"We don't know what's coming next. We don't have all the information. We've got to get to the command post and rally there. That's our order."

I shook my head and pulled back from the window. "All right, brother. We can take my van. Let's go."

Dan grabbed the only other people in the office—two agents—and we headed to the Street. What greeted us there was more apocalypse. White ash-covered office workers stumbled around, going nowhere, in shock. Some looked to us for help, while others walked around in confusion. We helped a few more and pointed others in the right direction for safety, then stepped around them and found my van. Despite the chaos, it was intact.

I put Sara in the passenger's seat and the three men in the back. It was crowded for them, with all the phones, weapons, ammunition, and food. But we weren't going too far.

No more than five minutes later, we arrived at the DEA's office and remained in the vehicle. Dan called for instructions and received new orders.

"We need to move farther out," Dan told us. "They have intel that more buildings may be attacked. The new command post is now aboard the USS Intrepid. It's located at Pier 86, right on the Hudson River. We need to get there as fast as we can and report to the SAC. Let's go."

Dan told us if we separated for some reason, we needed to keep in touch with the FBI. Things were changing rapidly. We couldn't become complacent and assume that the facts we had now would be the same two minutes from now.

I drove fast to Pier 86. A crowd milled around the gangway. At the top of the ramp sat the Intrepid. This decommissioned aircraft carrier had seen action in World War II and Vietnam. In 1982, it was brought here to be a museum. Right now, it would serve as our new command post.

We approached the SAC (Special Agent in Charge) and identified ourselves. He told us to grab our weapons and handle command-post security. "Check everyone coming onto the ship. We're setting up on the deck."

We went back to my truck and grabbed the Remington 870 shotguns and plenty of shells. I looped a sling over my shoulder. The sling carried an extra seven shells for the shotgun, which was loaded with five. Then, I strapped on my gear—a Sig Sauer in a hip holster, an assault knife on my thigh, and a reserve pistol in case I needed it. Over my head, I slipped on a vest that said, "Federal Agent." In seconds, I'd transformed from an undercover agent into a warrior. I was ready for anything.

Our small group quickly established security at the ship's entrance and along the starboard side. No one got past us without a proper ID.

After an hour of us handling security, the SAC gave us more bodies. This allowed me to go back to the truck and set up the Nextel units I had brought. I gave them to our people first, then other security personnel, until I ran out. The phones allowed us to communicate with each other while maintaining the security perimeter.

Periodically, we held security meetings in small groups. Our main threat was body bombs. A terrorist might come over to the Intrepid and blow himself up along with all of us. We pushed the security levels farther out from the entrance when we received more officers. This would minimize the damage a detonation would cause. Our mission was to protect the high-level folks in the command post.

I had been standing at a foot post for several hours when my group was called to the command post. By now, dozens of law enforcement agencies had flooded the Intrepid with officers. The SAC gave them the responsibility for security and called us to the command post.

I was awed by its size as I walked onto the long deck. Aircraft carriers are an engineering marvel.

Before I could see the SAC, a black helicopter surprised me by silently descending from the clouded sky. The second its wheels touched the deck, men dressed in black jumped out. They had no insignias and no patches. Each one carried tactical equipment that none of us had seen before. It was obvious they were part of some special ops program. Before I could say a word, they went below deck and disappeared.

The SAC finished his meeting and pulled us over to a tent. "Listen up," he said. "I need you folks to go below deck and man a hotline we've set up for leads. Take the calls and kick them up to the agent in charge. Tommy will show you where it is."

That was it. The meeting was brief.

Tommy led us to a nerve center deep within the Intrepid. The FBI had been busy. In barely a few hours, they had everything set up. They also had grief counselors and medics checking on everyone to ensure agents were fit enough to work.

We sat down and started taking phone calls. At first, there weren't many. The DOJ was in the process of contacting the media to blast out the phone number. While we had a little downtime, we got caught up on the news, learning all we could about the attack.

There were four hijacked commercial jets. One had crashed into the Pentagon, collapsing part of the building. It was still on fire. Another plane had been headed to Washington, D.C. but crashed in Pennsylvania. We already knew two planes had crashed into the two World Trade Towers, collapsing them. The entire morning had been devasting.

By now, we had heard that hundreds, if not thousands, of fellow citizens were likely dead. We were at war, and we didn't even know the identity of the enemy. Our leaders needed information. This hotline was the tip of the spear.

One problem we dealt with was the desire to return to Ground Zero and search for our buddies. All of us had people we knew who might be under the rubble. Yet the JTTF was in charge. They wanted only those specifically assigned to look for survivors. This was primarily firefighters and uniformed cops. We were criminal investigators (although many of us had previously been cops). Our skillset was needed to run the hotline leads.

"We need you to figure out who did this," they told us. "We have an unlimited pool of law enforcement officers and firefighters to search for survivors. But we have a limited supply of investigators. If you get killed, who's going to solve this crime?"

They were right. Let the uniformed officers there do their job. In fact, searchers had already found over a dozen people in the rubble. Incredibly, they had somehow survived a building falling down on top of them.

Our direct supervisor walked around the hotline area, slapping a wooden ruler on his palm. "Let the JTTF figure out who needs to be where. Just follow orders. The commanders above you have more information. Let them use it to make the best decisions."

He was right. My training had burned that into me. The best thing I could do was to follow orders and do my job. I was no different than the state trooper pulling someone over for a dangling license plate. And, hey, he caught Timothy McVeigh.

I handled Hotline tips for hours. We could always tell when the number had been blasted out. All the phones rang at once.

At some point, I took a break and went above deck to the surface. Again, I watched two black helicopters silently land, drop off more spec ops men loaded with gear, and take off into the darkened sky. I glanced at my watch. It was midnight. I had just crammed two lifetimes into fifteen hours. That's how it felt.

I went back down and worked another two hours before quitting and crashing to sleep in my undercover surveillance vehicle. Even though I was completely exhausted, I found sleep hard to come by. Adrenaline raced through my body as I wondered who would attack me in the van. I imagined terrorists all around, with body bombs, ready to blow me up. It was extremely hard to get to sleep, especially since I hadn't eaten anything.

Around six in the morning, I awoke. Stepping outside the truck, the world was different. Traffic in New York City was almost nonexistent. The sky, normally filled with commercial jets, was eerily silent. Rubbing my eyes, I lit one of the many cigars I kept handy, hoping to get myself going again.

I staggered around and found plenty of fresh coffee to guzzle. Then, my comrades joined me for breakfast. We knifed into cans of beans, corn, peas, and macaroni. I also passed out several MREs or meals ready to eat. It was a far cry from the Italian feasts I'd enjoyed during undercover operations. But it was better than nothing. MRE's are the meals we grew up eating in the military when we did field or training duty.

We ate like hungry soldiers on the battlefield.

By now, Sara had been cleaned up and was functioning. Dan was at the top of his game, barking orders and keeping us focused. With some food and a cigar, I was ready for another long day.

Before heading back to work, I tried calling my wife. The cell towers had been jammed the previous day because the primary antenna was atop the World Trade Center. Now, early in the morning, I was able to talk to her. She hadn't known if she was still married or a widow and was grateful to hear from me. After a short talk, it was back to the hotline.

The flood of tips steadily increased. Around noon, the agent in charge pulled me into a meeting room.

"We've identified possible suspects onboard the plane," he told a group of us. "I'm assigning you three to this lead. He had contact with one of the suspects. Go and interview him."

By "you three," he meant a female agent from the State Department, a young agent who had just graduated from the FBI academy, and me. We couldn't have been more different.

The three of us piled into an SUV and headed to Brooklyn. The man we were interviewing was a supervisor in human resources from a major corporation.

We located his apartment and went inside. He was extremely nervous about giving this information because he believed he'd be a target for retaliation. But, in the end, he was patriotic. It was something he could do for his country.

The man told us he'd interviewed who he believed was one of the suspected hijackers. He said he was angry and couldn't speak English, so he brought a translator with him. The translator tried to convince this manager to give this person a job at his company. This may have been part of a separate plot; we didn't know for sure.

After talking to him, the manager felt this man was too angry and wouldn't fit their company well. So, he'd denied him a job. Who knew how that decision may have altered our lives?

We traveled back to the Intrepid and collaborated on a written report. When we turned it in, they handed us another lead.

This lead had to do with three individuals who were suspected of having been part of the hijacking. We spoke with one of them and grabbed his statement.

Again, we made our written report, received a new lead, and ran out. This went on and on for several days. During this time, I went home twice as more agents from across the country migrated to New York. What a relief they provided!

On or about the eleventh day or so, I went back down toward Ground Zero. I was in shock and awe. Entire firetrucks were crushed by falling buildings. Steel girders sticking up from a deep hole. Officers and firemen climbed over the rubble. By now, they had pulled approximately 20 people from this disaster. That fact alone was amazing.

I stood on the very edge of the scene, gazing at the empty space. It was hard to fathom. From deep inside the earth, smoke rose from something still smoldering. A scene like that never leaves you.

My purpose for being here was to attend a meeting. I had been called down for a new assignment. I had no idea what it might be.

Once a large group of agents were present, the supervisor gathered us around him and explained that they needed to find the black boxes from United Airlines Flight 175 and American Airlines Flight 11. We were reassigned to the 59th Street Transfer Station. Now known as the "Disco Dump." It was there, we would search for the black boxes.

The supervisor introduced the agents who would train us on the special equipment that detected the boxes. One of them explained that the first line of defense was a sensor held on the end of a long pole. This sensor was passed over the rubble, hoping for a hit.

"Are we going to climb all over the rubble here looking for them?" an agent asked.

"No," the supervisor replied. "As you can see, cranes are pulling out debris and loading trucks. The trucks go to 59th Street. That's where the New York City Department of Sanitation Transfer Station is located. It's right off the West Side Highway. You'll scan the trucks before they dump their loads onto the barges."

The supervisor talked for a few minutes before releasing us to the trainers. He pulled me aside.

"Listen, Tony," he said, "this work is not easy. We've had other agents on this detail, but they've requested administrative leave.

You'll see a lot of stuff in there, including victims. I hope you're up to the task."

"I am!" I replied enthusiastically. "I'll find those black boxes, sir; if they're in there, I will find them." Those who know me know one thing. I am a patriot through and through. My blood isn't red; it's red, white, and blue. So, I couldn't wait to do what I could. I trained my whole life for this moment to serve my country in the greatest time of need.

"That's what I want to hear. Spend another hour out here with the trainers so you know what you're doing. Then, grab all the sensors you need and get out there."

"Yes, sir," I replied.

After feeling confident I understood the process, I took a group of agents with me to the sanitation transfer station. We began to work immediately.

My team was composed of agents from various federal agencies. I divided them up and began the mission of finding the black boxes.

One group was assigned to wave the wand over the dump trucks before they unloaded the ground-zero debris. I had the rest of us scan the dumped loads on the barges. They provided me with a cadaver dog and handler to search for human remains. If we discovered any evidence that appeared to be human remains, the K-9 would let us know.

Walking over debris made it almost impossible to maintain a sure footing. We often fell, scraping up our arms and legs.

The other issue was the smell. Jet fuel, sheetrock dust, and crushed cement—not to mention a wet electrical burning smell that has stayed with me to this day—nearly knocked us to our knees. There were no masks, so we breathed this all in without a filter.

During breaks, more than a few of us wondered about our long-term health. After all, there had to be radiation leaking from all the X-ray machines in the dentists' and doctors' offices. Between the radiation and the chemical dust, it was anyone's guess as to our projected life expectancy.

We turned off our thoughts and went back to work. We did what we had to for the country, the victims, and their families. I just couldn't stop thinking about the victims and their families; they needed answers, resolve, they needed to know. I was determined to get their answers. On top of that, we just needed to find out who committed this evil deed.

This work was challenging but rewarding. I assumed we had one of the harder jobs until I received the next assignment.

That one would test my soul.

Chapter 14

Ground Zero Evidence Recovery

As I said, work at the sanitation transfer station was tough. Sixteen-hour shifts were the norm. I saw victims' feet with shoes still on them. Bloody computers. Broken desks. Legal papers. Girders. Everything a 110-story office building held. Truck after truck after truck. They never ended.

After each shift, I tried to sleep. But the images stayed with me. I understood why so many people had tapped out.

Yet having spent three years as a Young Marine (instead of the Boy Scouts), followed by seven years at a military academy instead of a public elementary, middle school, and high school, then nine years in the military reserves, and now with roughly eight years on the job, I was a hard through and through. Tapping out would never cross my mind. In fact, I wanted to do more. Despite the lack of sleep, I felt like I should be hunting down those responsible myself.

To make the work more efficient, I erected some scaffolding so we could "wand" the dump trucks faster without having to climb up and down on a ladder. This sped up the process by at least a minute. When multiplied by 100 trucks, several more trips were added in the same amount of time.

As a leader of the detail for about a week, I spent a lot of hours doing the actual work. I did this for three reasons. First, I wanted to try and improve the system. The scaffolding was one change. Another was altering the pole, making it longer. This allowed for a greater reach. The second reason was to lead by example. I found I had better workers when they saw me sweating right beside them. I'm sure some folks can be great leaders from afar. But I'm a hands-on leader. As I've said, the third reason was that I desperately wanted to find these boxes and get answers for our country.

One afternoon, we sat on a bench during a break. Richie, one of the Agents on my team, had something on his mind.

"Tony, how powerful is this scanner?"

"The trainers told me it would penetrate at least twenty feet—maybe more, depending on the voids and composition of the material."

"That's pretty deep," Richie said. "It's got to be pretty powerful to do that."

"It is," I replied.

"What do you think it does to our family jewels?"

"What are you talking about?"

"Don't you think it might stop us from having kids?"

I rubbed my jaw.

"I can't imagine they'd do that to us. Thank God my wife is pregnant. I'm only having one kid, so I guess I'm covered no matter what."

Richie rubbed his crotch and shook his head. "Man, I don't know. I think I can feel this scanner shrinking my you know what's."

"Just focus on the work and don't worry about it," I told him calmly before turning around and checking out my own equipment. Everything seemed to be in order. But I did begin to worry about it.

By the third day of this work, they provided some ninety-nine-cent painter's masks to cut down on whatever we were breathing. Hey, it was better than nothing.

***

One day, I had a meeting at the command post. They asked how it was coming. I told them that I had no luck so far.

"Listen," the supervisor told me, "we will likely never find those boxes. They've probably been crushed, pulverized, or melted in the heat of the explosion and fires."

That was depressing to hear. The information on those black boxes could surely provide valuable evidence. The thought that we were wasting our time had me grinding my teeth. I was more determined than ever.

During this same meeting, they gave me additional duties.

"We're worried about the agents, officers, and even citizens taking souvenirs from the rubble. I want you to provide some security for the barge. Have some of your team inspect the process upon loading, then make sure it's offloaded properly. Got it?"

"Yes, sir," I replied.

They set this up when the barges we inspected floated to the Fresh Kills landfill in Queens to be offloaded for more forensic work. We had no idea what was going on up there because we had our hands full looking for the black boxes.

Now, I'd have to send some men on the barge until it was offloaded. This dramatically reduced our workforce, putting more strain on all of us.

I went back and organized the team, leaving out the part about not finding the black boxes. For the first trip, I sent Richie and another man. They were gone for hours. When the barge returned, Richie told me what was going on at the Fresh Kills Landfill.

"Tony, you're not going to believe what I saw," he said as he pulled me aside.

"Try me," I whispered.

"They have agents with rakes combing through piles of rubble—rock by rock—looking for DNA.... remains. Can you believe it?"

I closed my eyes and imagined the worst. "I guess there's no other way to do it."

"I'm not pulling a body part out of the rubble," he said. "No way."

"Look," I said, "thank God we have this job and not that one. I feel sorry for those poor guys. At least the rubble passes by us fast."

Richie nodded and got back to work. Undoubtedly, this attack would affect more than the victims' families. Many of the living would be hurt too.

***

Working on this detail, time lost all perspective. I worked and slept—nothing else. I didn't see it ever ending. There was too much rubble to remove.

During one of the meetings at the command post, the supervisor had news for me.

"Your team has been doing great work on the black box recovery detail. We're promoting you to a new detail."

My eyes opened wide in anticipation; a promotion was always good.

The supervisor picked up a piece of paper.

"I'm promoting you to evidence recovery. You'll be assigned right away. They'll get you lined up with your new duties."

"Wow!"

"Will I be conducting searches of suspects?"

"No," he replied, not making eye contact.

"This is more detailed work. Here are your new orders. Report to the agent-in-charge at the duty desk and do your best."

I took the orders and spotted the address at the top: Fresh Kills Landfill. My heart dropped.

"But, sir," I pleaded, "we're close to finding that black box. We can't give up on that."

"We aren't. I have a new team moving in behind you to take over."

I was prepared to keep talking more when his phone rang. He answered it and walked away. This told me the meeting was over.

Following orders, I told the all the agents at the same time. They each hung their heads. We stood there for a few minutes, letting it soak in. Then, we grabbed our gear and left. It was a quiet trip.

My first view of the Fresh Kills operation was another memory burned in my brain. A bulldozer dropped a pile of rubble in front of five agents and an NYPD Detective. Each agent was dressed in a white hazmat suit, or "bunny suit," as we affectionately called it. Brown rubber boots completed the outfit.

When a new pile was dropped in front of them, they grabbed their rakes and began pulling the rubble out, looking for evidence. There were about twenty stations like this. The bulldozers always picked up the searched rubble and brought over a new batch.

The agent-in-charge lined us out. The work was highly focused.

"We're only looking for DNA …yes, evidence…remains. If you find evidence, place it in the white bucket. Then call a cadaver dog and handler and wait for a hit. If the dog sits, its human remains. Then, bring it to the CSI station and grab a fresh bucket. It's pretty simple. Any questions?"

"No, sir."

"Good. Then go to station 11."

"Yes, sir."

That was the quickest training I'd ever had.

When we arrived at our station, I learned that an NYPD detective sergeant was in charge of our small group. He also supervised two other stations, floating around, answering questions, and watching the work. The five of us stayed on the ground and raked a new pile toward us from five separate directions. By spreading it all out, we could effectively pick out human remains.

Nearby, a desk sat out in the open. It was staffed by a CSI unit. On top of the desk was a white bucket. To start, I walked over and grabbed an empty bucket. Written on the side in black magic marker was "DNA."

When I arrived back at our station, my team slipped into our "bunny suits" and donned a mask. As the bulldozer approached, we backed up a few feet. That was a mistake.

A billowing cloud scattered in every direction when the load hit the ground. In seconds, we were covered with white dust. Several of us, including me, started coughing.

"That's your first lesson," the NYPD detective said. "Stand far away until the dust clears."

"Thanks," I said sarcastically. "Okay, guys, let's get to work."

No sooner had we started pulling debris out of the pile did we find something.

"Tony," Richie said. "Look at this. I think it's someone's finger."

Sure enough, it was a small finger bone with flesh still on it.

I signaled the detective. "We found a finger."

He waved for a dog to come over. "Let him have a sniff."

The dog came over and homed in on the finger bone. Then, to our shock, the dog picked it up.

"What the ….?!" I yelled.

The handler ordered the dog to release it.

"What kind of dog is that?" I yelled. "Eating a human finger!"

"Relax," the handler said. "He's trained to smell human flesh. He doesn't eat it."

"Then what was that?" I said, pointing to the bucket.

"A chicken bone, the various restaurants in the towers used loads of meat—mostly chicken and sushi. You'll find fish by the pound. We need the dog to tell the difference."

***

By the fifth day, the work had settled in. Rubble dumped. Dust cloud clears. Rake for twenty minutes. Collect DNA. The pile is removed. A new pile was dumped.

After a few hours of work each day, the painter's mask was covered with sweat, soot, and anything else that could stick to it. This made it hard to breathe, I knew whatever I was breathing in wasn't good, but we followed orders.

Whenever the sun fell below the horizon, they fired up banks of portable lights. Each bank was powered by a gasoline engine. In addition to everything else, we breathed in exhaust vapor all night.

Once my 16-hour shift was over, I could barely drive home. Unfortunately, they didn't allow me to drive home. Instead, I had to drive to the command post. It had recently been moved off the USS Intrepid to the U.S. Customs Office located 20 blocks down the West Side Highway. Once there, I reported to the supervisor and learned if they had more work for me.

I answered phones and ran errands for them. One time, they sat me down at a desk and had me check the IDs of people coming in. After I did this for a few minutes, a supervisor came over.

"Could you hold this spot for an hour?" she asked me.

"The person doing this job has got to eat. He needs a break."

"Sure," I said.

What else could I say? It was controlled chaos. Everything needed to be done. I was simply a body to be plugged in.

At no point did my shift ever end. It just kept going until I dropped. Then, they plugged another body in.

About two weeks after starting the evidence recovery detail, they had me perform dignitary protection service after my shift. VIPs and politicians arrived, wanting to see Ground Zero.

Sometimes, I took them to the edge of Ground Zero. Other times, we went to an adjacent building where an entire floor—the 20th— was dedicated to taking photos of Ground Zero. Everyone needed protection because we didn't know what might happen. Or who was still out there to kill us. It was a very unsettling time.

I handled a lot of dignitary protection, so many I can't recall. But I know one thing: each time I brought someone to Ground Zero, they broke down and cried. Every. Single. Time.

When I finally made it home, I would strip down in the hall and put my clothes in a plastic bag. Amy washed them separately or threw them out, depending on how bad they were. I went through a lot of clothes.

After stripping down, I took a shower, ate something, and fell into bed. Five hours later, the alarm went off, and I did it all over again. That's life in this line of work.

Trust me, it ain't like TV.

***

Day after day, the rubble never stopped coming. Each team member took a corner of the pile and raked it back. If we saw something unusual, we used our gloved hands to search for it.

On any given day, I might find a bare foot. The next day, a rib cage. The day after, I'd find a scalp with hair on it. Sometimes there were bones, and unfortunately, other times, human flesh. We found brain matter, eyes, and all parts of the body. It was never-ending and very sad. These were people, I thought, beloved souls, family members, someone's significant other.

I took time to kneel and say a prayer each time I found remains.

However, each time I found DNA evidence, I was excited. I knew a family member would get answers. They would know for sure what happened to their loved one. That was something for me to focus on.

Occasionally, we'd find some fire equipment like a boot or a helmet. That was an extremely sad moment too. These brave firefighters had answered the call of duty and died for it. The least we could do was return it to their family.

At the start of each shift, we had the same team members. But one day, they pulled a guy off and put him in charge of his own pile. To replace him, another agent arrived. After two hours of searching, she threw down her rake and tapped out.

"I didn't sign up for this," she said.

I turned to face her. "Well, guess what? None of us signed up for this, either. Our fellow citizens in the towers didn't sign up for this. Neither did their families. But we're at war. Pick up your rake and start digging!"

She shook her head. "I'm not doing it." Walking away, she headed for her car and left.

A handful of agents did that. Male. Female. Old. Young. It was the kind of work you couldn't possibly imagine performing when you applied for a job in law enforcement.

Over time, I learned if a new person could get through the first day, they had a 90 percent chance of making it. That first 16 hours was the test.

***

During the DNA recovery, I found many ID badges. Sometimes, I'd find a wallet with a driver's license inside. I would collect all of this in a separate bucket and take it to the desk. To my surprise and disappointment, they didn't want them.

"We only need DNA," they told me. "That's it. Just DNA."

I shook my head. This made no sense whatsoever.

Despite that order, I continued collecting them on the side. After a few days at the landfill, I took my bucket—half-full of IDs, wallets, and licenses—and walked over to the DNA desk. I let her have it.

"We should be collecting IDs," I said angrily.

"The families need to know."

Before she could speak, I went on.

"You guys are scooping up the pile when we're done, and it's going over to a crusher. We're losing these identification cards. This is a crime scene. Come on!"

"Orders are orders," she said. "No IDs."

I left in a huff and kept collecting them. The next day, a different supervisor looked in my bucket and took them from me. The day after that, they held a meeting for all twenty station leaders.

"New orders," the supervisor said.

"From now on, collect all forms of identification and put them in a separate bucket."

I puffed out my chest and strutted all the way back to my pile. Later, they assured me that my bitching had absolutely nothing to do with the new orders. They'd just decided to change course. I didn't believe that for a minute.

Unfortunately, this was the chaos, the fog of the situation. And now, some families somewhere would have answers.

***

After many days of being there, the clergy began showing up. We had Rabbis, Catholic priests, preachers, and all kinds of religious leaders. They walked around announcing, "If you guys need anything or want to talk about something, we're here."

A preacher from another state commented on the irony of doing this work here.

"What do you mean?" I asked him.

"You're looking for remains of dead right here," he said.

"So?" I replied, still confused.

"The place is called Fresh Kills Landfill. Does that sound normal to you?"

I stepped back and pondered that. As a native New Yorker, I'd heard the name Fresh Kills from birth. Not once did I ever think about where it came from. As my group kicked it around, a rabbi solved the mystery.

"The Dutch controlled parts of this area," he said. "When they found fresh water nearby, they named it on a map Fresh Kille. In

Dutch, Kille means waterway or river. Over time, the river became the Fresh Kills estuary. And, thus, this landfill is named after that river."

Okay. At least that explanation sounded better than "a convenient dumping ground for organized crime."

***

I had been working at the landfill for three months. Nothing fazed me anymore. When I found partial remains of a victim, I put it in the bucket and took it to the desk, grabbing a freshly washed bucket. Then, I walked back and kept raking. I was a machine. No emotions. No feelings. No thoughts. Just moving ahead, one foot in front of the other for the victim's families and my country.

This particular night, I'd found a piece of a victim's scalp and turned it in. When I returned to my pile, I continued raking. One of the prongs got stuck on something. I had to bend down and use my hands to dislodge it. Once I was down on my knees, I pulled a few rocks away and saw a large Ziplock bag with a ham sandwich inside. Next to it was a handful of potato chips. On the other side of the sandwich was a Diet Coke.

Pulling it from the rubble, I held the package up to the portable lights. Incredibly, the sandwich, which was wrapped in plastic wrap, was in perfect condition. So were the chips. The Diet Coke had a slight dent on it, but otherwise, it was completely intact.

This stunned me.

I lowered my body to the ground and sat on the dusty earth, contemplating this discovery. Someone had put it on their desk when they arrived at work. This was before the first plane struck. It had then survived the tower collapse. When the crane loaded it in the dump truck, it survived. And the dumping onto the barge. Once here, it was dumped on the landfill until, finally, it was scooped up and dumped in front of me.

What were the odds?

As I marveled at this miracle, I felt tears streaming down my cheeks. Then it hit me. This little package was a beautiful sign of love. After all, someone's wife, husband, significant other, loved one, or even perhaps themselves had probably gotten up and made this sandwich. They carefully packed it in a baggie with some chips and a soda. Then, they'd given it to this victim with a kiss before they left, never to return. I could actually feel the love oozing through the plastic.

Why did this lunch survive and not the person? Did this lunch belong to the evidence I'd found a few minutes earlier? This was my breakdown moment. I was done raking for evidence. It was time to take a break.

I picked up this baggie of love and carried it gingerly to a bench near the portable lights. I sat down and started taking in all my emotions.

"You okay, sonny?"

I lifted my head to find an Irish Catholic priest standing there. With a tear breaking the corner of my eye, I said, "Father, have you got a minute?"

"Absolutely," he said with a thick Irish brogue.

"That's what I'm here for, lad." He sat next to me.

"Father, I guess this is my moment." I showed him the untouched bag.

"All I've seen is disaster, response, a law enforcement officer's job, and everything that I've been trained for. There's no love in any of it. It's all terrorism. But now, for the first time, I've seen some love. I've seen the human side attached to all these remains."

He nodded, saying nothing. I continued.

"Father, this is love. Someone packed this lunch for their loved one and expected them to come back home after work. And they're not coming back. This was their lunch. They just wanted to work, have lunch, and come home to their family. This meal shows love. It's what separates us from the terrorists. That's why I'm overcome with emotion. I needed a timeout."

He looked at me, placed his hand on my shoulder, and said, "It's love, son—no doubt about it. Now, I want you to give that to me, and this is what you're going to do, lad. You're going to take a break for a bit and collect yourself. Then get back to work. You're going to find more evidence of love. Then, you're going to get in your car and go home at the end of your shift. You're not going to be putting on any radio stations or listening to any sad music. Do you understand me?"

"Yes, Father."

"You have a wife?"

"Yes, Father."

"You're going to get back to your house. You're going to eat dinner. You're not going to be turning on the television, either. You're not going to be watching any sad shows or any news reports. You're going to wash your clothes, clean up, and get straight to bed. Then, you're going to get your ass up first thing in the morning, eat a good breakfast, kiss your wife goodbye, and get your ass back here on time for your shift. You're going to finish the job, and you're going to do your job until you're told it's over. We are at war; if you don't do it, who will. Do you understand me?"

He shook my arm when I failed to respond fast enough.

"Do you understand me?"

"Yes, Father." I stepped back, stood up straight, and popped him a salute.

Muscle memory from my military days.

"Thank you," I said, getting to my feet and heading back to the pile. It was exactly what I needed to hear at exactly the right time.

That Irish priest straightened me out like nobody's business. My emotions were gone. I had a game plan. I was not allowed to listen to the radio and all those sad songs. I couldn't watch the horrible news programs. I had to get here each day and do my job. Because if I didn't do it, who else would?

He was right.

It was all hands-on deck. We'd talk about the love afterward when all this was over. My country needed me, and I was answering the call. I had the Watch. That was the love I could show my fellow citizens, the victims, and their families. And right now, they needed it.

To this day, I'm still doing what that priest told me to do in every aspect of my life; I am still on the job after 30 years of serving my country: Doing my job until my shift is over, maintaining the Watch.

Then, another shift begins, an off-duty one.

And I will do it as long as I am physically able.

Chapter 15

The Spirit of the Pipes

For the most part, our job is thankless and usually requires jumping right in the middle of an existing situation that involves some form of conflict —seeing it and dealing with it. When we're called, something terrible happens. We're there to stop the conflict, not receive love or praise. However, the untold reality is, we are peacemakers and seek nothing more than peace. But when it comes down to it, we are always the protectors', ensuring society is safe so others may enjoy peace.

Now and then, though, a cop gets a glimpse of love and a feeling of overwhelming peace. For me, seeing that perfect sandwich bag was what I needed to know, that love still exists in the world and peace was inevitable.

There were other examples of love. Early on, when I escorted dignitaries to Ground Zero, citizens lined up for blocks holding signs saying, "We Love You! Keep Going."

It was emotional for me; I broke "tear," as we say in the business, as I drove up the west side highway. Those signs gave me the strength and determination to keep going.

Love also arrived in the form of food. Hundreds of sandwiches were delivered continuously to Ground Zero, the command post, and Fresh Kills.

When I worked the black box detail at the sanitation transfer station, we received sandwiches from delis all over the New York in New Jersey metropolitan areas. They were wrapped in butcher paper, and the sandwiches, often called "wedges" by us native New Yorkers (we called it a wedge because the bakery used to call the sub bread a "wedge" of bread), were delivered in small boxes.

The first time I opened one, the butcher paper had a message from workers at the deli saying how much they loved us, urging us to keep going. Sometimes, there were poems or a special note of encouragement. No matter the form of the message, it was always memorable and inspiring—just another example of the incredible outpouring of love we received while working hard for peace and justice. It was an act of kindness I will never forget.

Thank you to everyone who did that for us; it meant everything.

***

As I said before, the work at Fresh Kills landfill was an endless assembly line. Once a pile had been raked out and examined, we waited for another dozer to replace it. There were small pockets of downtime while waiting for the next dozer to arrive. The atmosphere was extremely solemn, but we would use these small opportunities to talk to a coworker. If that wasn't an option, we would stand around contemplating what had happened and what would happen going forward.

One of those moments involved a fellow Agent and friend, Agent John Stone. He happened to be in my detail.

218

John worked right next to me, digging through his slice of the pile. One day, we had a conversation that would change my life.

"Tony, how many kids do you have?" John asked.

"I don't have any kids yet. Thankfully, my wife survived the attack. She's pregnant right now with our son."

"Do you plan on having any more kids?"

"We're only having this one," I replied.

"My wife and I are both career people, so I don't want to shortchange a kid by bringing more into the world."

John pushed back his hard hat.

"You told me you're Catholic. Catholics are supposed to have as many children as possible. That's what our religion wants you to do: make kids."

"Sure," I said, "but I'm also a responsible thinker. If I can't afford children and take care of them properly, I will not bring them into the world. That's irresponsible."

John waved his arm over the endless pile of sacred Twin Tower rubble.

"Look around you, Tony. This is a devastation we have never seen in our lifetimes. Look at what's happening to the world. You may not want to bring another child into this world, but you have to."

"Why?"

I asked, dumbfounded; why would a colleague dive this deeply into my private life.

"In case this happens again, and one of your children dies in the attack," John said softly. "You'll at least have another."

I stepped back in astonishment at his statement.

"Yeah," he continued, unfazed.

"And besides, a kid needs a brother or sister to play with. Otherwise, they'll grow up messed up; kids need a brother or sister."

John kept talking about this issue. For some reason, I didn't stop him. The more he talked, the more he made sense. By the time the next truckload came, I had decided to have a second child. Aidan Michael was the result.

Aidan turned out to be one of the brightest souls in the universe. I call him my special son because of an instance shortly after birth when he coded out and was brought back to life. I can't imagine life without him. And his life is due to that conversation with Agent Stone.

But first, Amy had to give birth to the son she was carrying. Five months after 9/11, Anthony Marshall was born. When I first held him in my arms, I kissed his cheek and wondered what kind of world he was coming into.

Could a simple person like me make it better for him?

It was a heavy burden, but one I was determined to carry.

***

I told Amy to head north past the power plant the morning of the attack.

"You must be at least 35 miles away from Indian Point. Go north as far as you can. You should be okay."

"I'm not leaving you," she said. I couldn't believe what I was hearing.

She fought me tooth and nail, and in the end, she remained to support me. She was there for me when I dragged in from each 16-hour shift. At some point, we were able to discuss the close call she'd lived through.

Amy worked for the US Department of Labor. Her office was on the same floor as mine in Six World Trade. If she had not gotten away when the second plane hit, she would not have survived when the North Tower crashed into the building, cutting it in half. Unfortunately, the million dollars' worth of high-tech surveillance equipment I maintained was saved because it was in an alternate storage location.

Being able to go home each night to my wife was a pleasure many involved in this tragedy couldn't experience. I was so thankful she had survived.

Each night, I trudged home, took a shower, and downloaded my feelings to her. Just having someone listening was healing. She gave me the strength to get up each morning when the alarm bell rang.

Early on, Amy noticed I was encountering some stomach issues. She insisted I go to Mount Sinai Beth Israel Hospital and let the doctors check me out. Sure enough, my ulcer had flared up again. They asked me what I'd been eating.

"The mornings were frantic, and schedules changed so frequently that often we did not have time for a solid breakfast," I told them. "Maybe some beef jerky or military meals ready to eat (MREs) during the day."

"Any solid food?" the Doctor asked.

"A wedge sandwich when a delivery showed up. That's pretty much it."

The Doctor shook his head and frowned. He launched into a proper diet and how it worked with the human body. I listened and promised to do better. Then, I downed some prescription pills and went back to the battlefield. I had no choice. We were informed this was a "War Time" mission.

Unfortunately, I was back at the hospital a few months later. During my digging at Fresh Kills, I often lifted girder beams to inspect underneath. My back began hurting. When it got bad, Amy insisted I see the Doctor.

The Doctor examined me and told me to take it easier on my back. They handed me bottles of muscle relaxers and pain pills, patted me on the head, and sent me back to Fresh Kills.

As the days dragged on, Amy had a front-row seat to my aches and pains. She continually pushed me to go back to the Doctor for checkups.

Shortly after 9/11, Amy had a new office working north of Canal Street in lower Manhattan. Because she was pregnant, the government refused to let her work below Canal Street. I looked over some of her paperwork and learned the EPA considered the area a dangerous toxic zone for pregnancies. It didn't, however, meet the standards of men like me who weren't pregnant.

Danger to one's health is another aspect of being a law enforcement officer. Unfortunately, we must always encounter significant risks to our lives. That's the job. And we do it without question.

I have always said, "We were born to do this job; it's a calling, not a choice. It's your life's contract."

It's our Sacred Obligation.

***

Management rotated us in and out to keep us from tipping the scales emotionally. I often pulled duty at the command post, where I answered phones for investigative tips, handled security, ran leads, and escorted dignitaries to Ground Zero.

After several months of working at Fresh Kills and various rotation duties, I started doing more street work. Sgt. Frank Rose, an NYPD detective out of the fifth precinct in Chinatown, was my partner. We became very close.

Frank and I ran leads from the FBI Joint Terrorism Task Force. When they ran out of work, I headed back to Fresh Kills to dig. But it was usually for no more than a week. Because I'd soon be back with Frank, running more leads.

After 9/11, my life as a jack-of-all-trades lasted for almost a year. By then, the digging and leads were petering out. HUD Inspector General pulled me back to my regular job. There were no goodbye hugs or tears. I simply went back to my job and saw new friends like Frank when I could.

Besides, I was dragging a bit, tired for several weeks on end; I'd worked straight, sometimes 16-hour days. It felt both patriotic and exhausting.

I took a few days off here and there. One task I was called to do during my off time was funerals. Not work them. I played the bagpipes; I was a "Piper."

In 1996, I became inspired by the "spirit of the pipes" during a march up 5th Ave for the St Patrick's Day parade. I decided to take up Bagpiping. The only problem was my name was Italian! My mother was English, Irish, and German Jewish. But nonetheless, I decided to explore my Celtic heritage and learn the bagpipes. And I liked wearing a dress, ahh, hmmm, I mean a kilt.

I took classes from Seamus Coyne and the Coyne School of Piping and Drumming. Seamus was one of the best bagpipers in the world and placed top in the world for the solo piping championships a few years prior to my meeting him. Once I had the hang of it, I played as many venues and events as I could.

I call bagpiping a hobby because I've never charged for a performance. I felt God had bestowed this gift on me, the talent of being able to play, so it was my job and duty to give back to people who also yearned for the spirit of the pipes.

I bagpiped for the first anniversary 9/11 Memorial Service held in lower Manhattan, sponsored by the Federal General Services Administration at 26 federal plaza federal office building in lower Manhattan. A host of dignitaries from around the government attended, including staff from the New York City Mayor's Office.

After 9/11, I donated my time and talent to many funerals, some of which were associated with those who perished. I was also designated as the official bagpiper for the HUD's Office Inspector General in Washington, DC. As a matter of fact, I played for the Inspector General's mother's funeral. It was a great honor.

I routinely pipe the casket in the church and then out after the ceremony is over. Then it's over to the cemetery, where I select a high point or a grassy knoll in the distance from which to play. We do this so we don't become the center of the ceremony. It's our job simply to accent the ceremony.

Over the years, I've had unforgettable memories from all the events I piped at. It has been a true labor of love and a great opportunity to help contribute to bringing the "spirit of the pipes" to the world.

***

My seventh anniversary with HUD Inspector General came and went. I was back doing my high-speed, low-drag undercover work, electronic surveillance, and wiring up other undercover cops. By this time, I had spent over 5 years undercover. 9/11 changed how I saw the world as it related to my mission to serve and protect. I wanted to be more involved in work that would prevent another terrorist act from occurring. So, I started looking on USAJOBS, the government's premier employment website. I really felt a strong desire to now fight the war on terror.

I learned of a position with the Department of Defense in California. The old Fort Ord Military Installation had been "BRAC'd" or suffered the effects of the Base Realignment and Closure Committee. The Installation was shut down and sold off into 4 parcels, each for a dollar, to the neighboring towns. The civilian Department of Defense Police force that was already in place for the military was then used and expanded to serve the neighboring towns through a Memorandum of Agreement for Public Safety Services. This department, the Presidio of Monterey Police Department, needed a Police Captain and SWAT commander.

They really liked my work during 9/11 and my previous work in the military as well. This got me a little closer to the war on terror and came with captain's bars. Reading the job description, I was hooked. If I got it, I would take it.

I researched everything I could about the area. Then, I interviewed and waited. Sure enough, I landed the job. This was my first job as a supervisor in the government. I had always been in positions of leadership, but now, I have achieved becoming a government supervisor.

It was a melancholy day when I turned in my badge to the Inspector General and said goodbye to everyone. So much of my life and career had been with HUD Inspector General as an Agent, especially the events of 9/11 and the years I spent undercover. I had been exposed to and involved in so much and made many friends. It was hard to let go.

On the way out to California, I thought about the mission I was leaving behind. We never found the black boxes. And even though we knew who attacked us, we hadn't yet captured the ringleader— Osama Bin Laden. So much was still left to do.

During a stop in Oklahoma, I came out of the restroom and saw a Coca-Cola truck delivering soda to the store. Since I was traveling alone, I struck up a conversation with the driver. He let me sit in the truck for a few minutes, so I could reminisce. For a moment, I was seven years old again and back in the truck with my father.

"Anthony, be careful what you say at this stop," My father warned me.

"These are wise guys."

"What's a wise guy?" I asked.

"Someone who lives by a code and ensures you abide by it. They don't play around. Instead, the last thing you see is the last thing you'll see if you step outta line—if you're lucky."

My father taught me his unique language. When delivering Coca-Cola, they weren't really called "stops." They were accounts, he said, and he wasn't a truck driver. Instead, he was a businessman who happened to drive a truck to facilitate his business. My father made sure I had this clear. As I absorbed the terminology, I memorized the route.

Whenever my father let me go with him, I was always excited. He and his "shaper" would occupy the two seats with me in the middle. The truck had this huge shifter. Every time my Dad shifted, the knob came between my legs, dangerously close to my chicken nuggets. Each time, I said, "Whew," and felt that I skirted another occasion of losing my manhood. Funny, though, I really felt like one of the guys, no matter how often they chuckled when that shifter came down.

At each stop, he'd tell me whether or not I could get out of the truck. Some places were too sketchy. And, some days, we'd find a restaurant damaged. Other times we'd find a business closed. My father explained that the owners had either failed to pay the wise guys or had refused to deal with them. Wise guys could stop shipments from coming to a store or the air coming to your lungs. Some places were just off-limits.

"We're not going in there," my father would tell me, "because they won't be in business much longer. Word on the street is they didn't pay their dues."

Sure enough, he was right; they were out of business two or three weeks later.

My father was like the mayor on his Coca-Cola route in New York. Everyone waved at him; the town adored him. That made me proud to be his son. He knew how to get along with everyone, he respected his customers and friends, and they respected him.

Along his route sat several confectionary stores. They had a rack of candy that was never sold. This baffled me. As a result, they were continually dusting off the candy and chips. We stocked colas in their refrigerated unit, but I was always left scratching my head. I never saw any customers; nothing was selling, but someone was either drinking or taking the soda we delivered.

Behind the counter was a curtain. I was never allowed behind that curtain.

My father gave me explicit instructions to leave the delivery of soda by the cooler.

"Do not go in the back!" he said, and "don't worry about getting paid; I will take care of that."

My father eventually told me that in the back was a large area—a "numbers joint" for gambling.

If you were playing the numbers, you'd walk up to the counter and hand over your ticket. Sometimes, they'd take a bet on the size of the crowds at the local racetracks. Whoever came the closest won. There wasn't any regulation of these games, so there was no telling how much they kept. Despite everything, after the gamblers were told they weren't close enough to the winning number, no one ever complained. Besides, also collocated in the back room were a handful of Italian ladies cooking the best marina sauce you ever put your lips to. If I was lucky, one of them knew I was there, and they brought me out a "Sauce roll." A Sauce roll was a freshly baked wedge of Italian bread filled with marinara sauce and little pieces of meatballs and sausage. The most incredible thing you have ever tasted.

My father had machines and coolers everywhere, even at police stations. I learned a lot about marketing when it came to delis, supermarkets, stationery stores, and confectionaries.

Eventually, I could tell when a store opened up whether it would make it or not.

By the time I was in my early twenties, I loved marketing. Yet being a cop is not marketing.

Or is it?

One day soon, I'd learn how to apply that knowledge to police work.

But first, I'd have to survive California.

Chapter 16

"Captain, my Captain"

The drive to California was long. I arrived around 4 p.m. and wanted nothing more than to eat a nice meal, shower, and go to bed early. Unfortunately, I had no shower. The main reason was I lacked a place to live. It was a problem that needed solving, at least before nightfall.

My car rolled to a stop outside of the police station, and a man approached my door. "Hello," he said. "Are you Tony Losito?"

"I am," I replied. "And you are?"

"Sgt. Chet Hogart."

"Well, Sgt. Hogart, I need two things: a good meal and a hot shower. Can you help me out?"

"I can," he said with a smile. "Let's eat first. I'll drive."

We walked over to his car and took off. A few minutes later, we pulled up to a Tex-Mex restaurant. It was decent—barely.

With a toothpick between my teeth, I asked him to take me to a supermarket. Once there, I strolled through the aisles shopping, talking, and joking with the clerks like a true New Yorker. We're friendly, and mix it up with everybody, always bringing our New York charm everywhere we go.

When I checked out, I joked with the cashier too. As I reached into my back pocket for my wallet, I caught a glimpse of the sergeant. He had his hands over his head like something was wrong. The clerk handed me the groceries, so I loaded him up.

We made our way to the car, giving me a chance to question him.

"Was something wrong back there?"

"Yes," he replied sternly. "Captain, we don't do that here."

"Do what?" I asked, concerned I'd committed some faux pas.

"Talk to people," he said, staring out the windshield.

This was probably some prank. "Are you kidding me?"

"No," he said, "I'm not. We just don't do that here."

I shook my head. "I'm from New York. We talk to people, and we show love. It's how I'm built."

He frowned, saying nothing. I wondered what I'd gotten myself into.

"Shall I take you to where you're staying?" he finally said.

"Sure," I replied.

He drove to the police station parking lot and stopped. I raised my eyebrows.

"I hope you're not putting me in a cell."

"No, sir," he replied somberly.

"Am I sleeping out in the parking lot?"

"Yes, sir."

I smiled. Now, I knew this must be a joke. Spoofing the new guy is standard operating procedure in Cop Land. I decided to play along.

"Sounds good!" I said enthusiastically.

We exited the car, the sergeant loaded with groceries and me following him. He walked around several police vans to a rusted and sun-scorched RV.

"Is this it?" I asked, pretty sure he wasn't kidding.

"Yes, sir," he replied. "It's a mobile home."

"It's an RV," I said. "There's a difference. One is a home. The other is a vehicle. This one has an engine."

"Yes, sir," Hogart replied in a low voice.

"Does it have a shower?" I asked sarcastically.

"Yes, sir. It has a shower."

"But it doesn't have a bathtub."

"But there's hot water, and it should get the job done."

I was secretly hoping it had a bathtub too. Try relaxing while standing up …you knucklehead! I thought to myself.

He hauled over my suitcases and helped me put away the groceries. After depositing the keys into my hand, he left.

I looked around the place, depressed; I lived like a hippie. After sulking for a few minutes, I put away my clothes. Then, I eased into the shower, which made a "phone booth" seem spacious.

As a trickle of lukewarm water dribbled over my skin, I used my detective skills to examine a half-used bar of soap. It was embedded with another man's curly chest hairs, the last renter, or so I assumed.

When I stepped out, I grabbed a fresh towel they had left for me. It, too, had curly chest hairs all over it, "ehh, whatta ya gonna do" I thought; I am lucky enough to have a roof over my head at the moment.

I was exhausted. I sat on the edge of the bed and leaned back, the creaking and groaning of the springs telling its own story. Eyes fixed on the ceiling; I imagined the thousand conjugal visits that had likely taken place on this bed. Right before I passed out, I knew Job One was finding an affordable place to live. I wasn't about to spend my life in this old RV.

***

Even though I technically worked for the Department of Defense, I was a captain and SWAT commander on the Presidio of Monterey Police Department. Behind the scenes, I was being groomed for the Chief of police position because the current Chief was looking to

233

move up to a Director position as he explained to me just before I arrived.

The purpose of the Presidio of Monterey Police Department was to protect the military servicemen and women, civilians working nearby for the Department of the Army and Department of Defense, and government critical infrastructure around the area. The servicemen and women resided with their families in mixed-use housing developments.

The police department also protected the Naval Postgraduate School housing area and the Defense Language Institute (DLI). The DLI is where all the language training for the Department of the Army occurs.

The Army base was Fort Ord. It was huge—one of the biggest in the Army. Clint Eastwood had received his basic training at Fort Ord and served as a lifeguard there.

Before arriving, I'd learned the Defense Department had BRAC'd the base. BRAC is an acronym for Base Realignment and Closure. The government sold off portions of the base to surrounding cities. Because the cities lacked the police and emergency services to handle these areas, they contracted with the federal government to have our police department provide those services.

After the BRAC had occurred and the neighboring towns purchased their slice of the base, each town grew double in size overnight. That meant each of us had to become State certified to enforce civilian law within these new jurisdictions.

I had researched this position carefully before taking it. It was an incredible job. I was a police captain performing both civilian and military law enforcement. Being a captain is one of the best ranks in the police department. If I wanted, I could step into the action or stand back and manage the situation. But I had to be very careful and not tower over officers in the field; it tends to intimate them if a supervisor is hanging over their shoulder.

I have always been of the assertion that a good leader trusts their people.

The department had about 80 employees. There was a director of emergency services, a police chief, one major, two captains, three lieutenants, three sergeants, and some detectives; the rest were patrol officers.

Before I could show up for work, I had to attend a two-week SWAT Commander School conducted by a former founding member of the FBI SWAT team but now retired.

During the training, I learned California had the highest rate of child abductions at that time. With a son who would soon be joining me, I was concerned about that fact.

Once I completed SWAT school, I had to attend Police Commanders Leadership School. Two retired female police chiefs ran it. They ran one of the best leadership programs I have ever attended. They were amazing instructors.

After completing my training, I found a place to live nearby and moved my meager possessions out of the RV. The RV was set up in the lot for Officers that transferred in from out of State, so I was grateful, and it served the purpose, but I didn't want to live in the parking lot for my tenure. It was a magnet for questions and problems from cops who couldn't find an officer on duty.

"It's two in the morning, so that means Captain Losito is in the RV. Let's just ask him."

No, thank you.

During all this training, I talked to Amy every day. She was working in New York City for the Department of Labor. Three times a week, she took the train to work. The other two days, she teleworked from home. We hoped she could eventually transfer to California.

I couldn't wait!

***

The first day I reported for duty, I was called into the police chief's office. William "Bill" Collins, the man who had hired me, had some things to get off his chest.

At six-foot-three inches, this gentleman from Indiana was quite the character. He had a dry sense of humor, never laughing or cracking a smile. When I walked in, Bill used his long arms to point me in the right direction. "Come on in and sit down on the couch there," he said. Every word was accompanied by waving arms and pointing fingers. Saying nothing, I followed his orders.

"I'm from Indiana," he said. "Real men are from Indiana, not the streets where you come from. You know why I hired you?"

"I'm not a real man, so I wouldn't know."

"Don't get all horse's ass with me," he said, pointing and waving. "I make the jokes around here."

I decided to cut to the chase. "Alright, Chief, why did you hire me?"

"Because you see all those characters out there?" he said, pointing out the office window to the lobby.

"You mean the officers and employees?"

"Exactly! I have no idea how to talk to those people. I hired you so you could be my voice and communicate with them."

I smiled. "Sort of like Aaron speaking for Moses." His brow furrowed as I continued. "Look, Chief, these are your employees. How do you run this operation if you can't communicate with them?"

He explained the employees didn't understand him or what he was about. He had spent six years in South Korea as Captain in the U.S. Army, much of it in the DMZ waiting to be shot. It was tough duty for anyone.

The Chief needed help from Donaldson, his major and deputy chief. Like Bill, Donaldson had also transitioned from active duty to civilian policing. For some reason, he didn't see eye-to-eye with Bill.

According to Bill, Donaldson was a stick-in-mud-type guy.

I thought about what Bill was saying. Donaldson, a Colonel, outranked me. There wasn't much I could do. And the Chief wasn't done complaining.

"I also have to tell you," he said, waving and pointing out his window, "we have an Officer who is a transvestite. He's a police officer who likes to dress in women's clothes under his uniform and after work."

"Chief, he's a police officer. He can wear women's clothes on the job as long as it's under his uniform."

"I'm telling you; he puts on women's clothes after work and comes back to the department just so I can see him."

"Okay," I said, unsure how to handle any of this. "I'll do my best."

I nodded.

"That's all I've got for you right now," he barked. "Now, get the hell out of my office."

I sighed.

Welcome to the Presidio of Monterey Police Department.

***

I spent the morning arranging my desk and getting office supplies. After lunch, a sergeant came into my office.

"Captain Losito, is it alright if I bring in a friend of mine who works for me? He wants to talk to you."

"Sure," I said. "Do you want to make an appointment?"

"He really wants to talk to you now," the sergeant said, shifting from foot to foot.

"Okay," I said. "Bring him in."

A few minutes later, a patrol officer stood at my door. He was tall and thin, his uniform crisp and polished. Next to him was the sergeant.

"Can I shut the door?" the sergeant asked.

"Sure," I replied.

"This is Arturo," the sergeant said. "He has something to tell you."

"You going to quit, Arturo? I've been here four hours, and you're going to drop your pink slip on me?"

"There's a pink slip involved," he said, smiling, "but not that kind."

I pointed to the chairs, and they took a seat. "Okay, what do you need to tell me?"

"I heard you were from New York City, so I know you must have a broad sense of understanding. You see the entire world in New York City. I figure you're very progressive."

He took a deep breath, glancing at the sergeant and back to me. "I like to wear women's clothes."

I rubbed my eyes. "Where do you wear women's clothes? At home?"

"Yes," he said, "sometimes I dress as a woman after work. But I also wear women's clothes underneath my uniform."

"Does it show?"

"No, it doesn't show." He pulled up his slacks so I could see his pink socks. Then, he stood up and pulled out a patch of underwear.

239

As he started unbuttoning his shirt, I stood up and raised my hand. "Okay, that's enough. You don't have to take off any more of your clothes."

"Are you okay with this?" he asked hesitantly.

I rubbed my jaw, weighing out everything. "Yeah, I'm okay with it."

"Some people call me a transvestite, cross-dresser, or transexual. Are you okay with that?"

"Yes, of course, just so long as you do your job as a police officer."

Arturo began to celebrate in my office, very elated. "I knew you'd understand!" he shouted. "I told everybody when you got here this would be a much better place for me. I was going to retire early, but now I'm going to stay on."

When he finally calmed down, I said, "Not a problem. Where I am from in New York, I grew up living and working with people of all races, creeds, colors, ethnicities, gay, straight, whatever you can think of; we celebrate everyone's choices and backgrounds. The best part is we all love and respect each other; it's one big melting pot."

Then I told him that I had a secret to tell him. "Can you keep it to yourself?"

"Absolutely," he replied. The sergeant also agreed as they both leaned in.

"Good," I said in a whisper. "The truth is, I'm a metrosexual."

Arturo's jaw dropped. "I promise I won't tell anyone. Your secret is safe with me. I won't tell a soul."

We both laughed! "Good One" he said.

The next day, Arturo came into my office holding blueprints.

"What's this about?" I asked.

"It's a plan for a third bathroom. I'll feel more comfortable changing in there."

I looked it over. I knew what stuff cost in New York City. I figured California had to be close.

"Arturo, this is a major construction project. It'll cost at least $100,000. I'll need to see if we have that in the budget."

He left my office with a smile on his face. Once the door closed, I placed my hands over my head and slapped myself. This was exactly what the Chief was concerned about. I wasn't looking forward to running this by him.

I waited until after lunch and went to see the Chief. He was walking around his office using a cane. He suffered from bad hips due to jumping out of planes in the military. He needed hip replacements, but instead, he kept putting off the inevitable surgery.

"What did I tell you about this guy?" the Chief said after studying the blueprints spread out over his desk. "I told you not to listen to him. Don't give him an audience. Don't give him anything."

"I can't ignore him Chief, he's a human being, and our employee. Do we have the money in the budget for this kind of renovation?" I asked sheepishly.

"Of course, we don't.

People think I can sit on the toilet and "crap" out $100,000. They don't live in reality like I do."

He stared through the blinds. "Come here. Check out this blonde."

I went to the window and saw a blonde woman in a dress holding a purse.

"She looks nice. What about her?"

"That's Arturo!" Bill screamed in my ear. "He just got off duty!"

"That's Arturo?" blinking several times.

"I told you he dresses like a woman. Now, he comes back here to taunt me, standing in line to get his car registered. Oh my God, I can't believe it's getting worse."

Before the Chief blew a gasket, I went and helped Arturo with his registration. I told Arturo that I would talk to him about his request for a separate bathroom after work.

I asked Arturo to meet me at a local restaurant after work to discuss his request. Arturo said, "I just want you to know that I'm not a homosexual," Arturo offered after we ordered. "I have a wife and three children. I dress like this because my mother wanted a girl when I was young. To hide her disappointment, she dressed me up like a girl. That's why I manifest as a girl. It feels comfortable."

I listened and was very understanding. Arturo was a good person. I told him so.

Eventually, the night was over, and I made my way home.

The next day, the Chief heard I'd been to dinner with Arturo. He ordered me to his office. So, this time I decided to have some fun.

"At the restaurant, was he still dressed up like a woman?" the Chief asked as he dangerously swung his stick around.

"Yep," I said, watching his expression. "And he brought his wife and three children."

"Oh my God," Bill moaned. "He's married? That poor wife. Is she a blonde like him?"

"No. She dresses up like a man."

He smashed the stick into his desk. "I knew it! This world is turning to shit. Complete shit!"

"Yeah, and his two boys dress up like girls."

"I don't want to hear anymore," he said, closing his eyes and looking away. Then, he tossed out one more question. "How does his daughter dress?"

"Like a mini police officer."

"That's it. I'm gonna retire and leave all this for you to sort out. Hand me that Vicodin."

I told him he needed to be more understanding; people are beautiful no matter how they appear, and God makes everyone perfect. But that didn't seem to fly.

The Chief didn't retire. And Jose was careful to stay away from him. All was well.

Until Christmas.

I was in the lobby putting up a Christmas tree when the Chief ambled by.

"What's all that?" he asked, pointing to some colorful cloth.

"Kwanzaa decorations," I replied.

"What the hell is Kwanzaa?"

"It's an African American holiday. We should recognize it and do our best to celebrate everyone's holiday traditions."

"Are those chocolates part of that?"

"No. We have four Jewish employees. Those are dreidels for their holiday."

"Oh, no. This is all backfiring on me."

I think he liked the drama, all the moaning and bitching. It was part of his comedic "Shtick" or role. Kind of reminds me of the Police Lieutenant, Frank McRae's character in the 1993 movie, "The Last Action Hero" starring Arnold Schwarzenegger. A similar loud and funny yet frustrated disposition. It kept employees away, which was what he wanted. Somehow, he made it through, and I know I broadened his look on life even if he didn't admit it.

Ultimately, he had a very big heart; he just had a hard time showing it.

***

Despite the Chief's frustrations, we did manage to perform some policing for the citizens. Bomb threats were a big part of our routine. Apparently, folks who didn't want to go to work made up a small percentage of those who called them in. That allowed me to roll out the entire SWAT team. We looked around for explosives until lunchtime. Once we cleared the area, it opened back up, and the people returned to work.

We were always on high alert because the military bases in Monterey were well known, and there were always protestors that did not like the military presence in the area.

Although, when not dealing with those issues, we routinely responded to domestic disturbances, suicides (which unfortunately did occur in the military), routine shoplifting calls, medical emergencies, and cougar calls.

Yes, cougar calls. Cougars were sighted quite often out by Fort Ord and would occasionally roam down to the residential areas.

One big caper we worked on was the theft of copper from abandoned military buildings. The Army had yet to remove it, so some local thieves saved them the trouble. It took us a few weeks, but we eventually caught the vandals.

Another caper involved my son. The Department of Labor had finally transferred Amy to nearby San Francisco. It was heaven, having my family all in one place.

Three days a week, Amy drove up to San Francisco. She would drop Anthony off at daycare. If she couldn't make it back in time to pick him up, I'd handle it.

I knocked off work one afternoon and swung by to pick up my son. He was in the aftercare area for parents who ran late. I walked up to the door and peered through the vertical window, not wanting to interrupt a lesson. A TV with a tape deck sat on the teacher's desk with a video playing. The video was designed to mesmerize the children.

Anthony was at the very back, cupping his hands to his ears. He was almost three but had some hearing issues. I watched as he got up and said something to the teacher. When she didn't respond, he walked to the TV and turned up the volume.

Suddenly, the teacher jumped up and slapped his hand away. Then, to my shock, she placed her hand on his chest and pushed him backward. He fell, hitting his head on the floor. I was beside myself.

I pushed open the door and lifted my screaming son from the floor.

"Don't you ever touch him again!" I yelled. "Stay right where you are."

Her eyes widened as she studied my uniform in disbelief. How rare is it for a cop to be standing there when you commit a crime?

"I'm so sorry," she said. "I didn't do anything."

"I saw what you did. I watched from the window in the door." I pointed to the ceiling. "And the cameras up there caught it too."

Realizing she was busted; she went to Plan B: crying.

"Don't touch any of the students here," I barked. "I'll be back in a second with the principal."

I carried my son to the front office, grabbing every manager I could find. When I told them what had happened, they were appalled. They put a substitute in the room and took the teacher to review the video; they saw the evidence. Then, they terminated her.

When I told Amy, she was lit too. And Amy is someone you don't want to meet in the octagon.

After they assured us, they would put extra teachers to watch over him, we left Anthony in that same daycare. That calmed us down tremendously. Besides, if we had moved him, it could've happened again.

Nobody messes with my son. Nobody!

***

Doris Day, another celebrity, lived in Carmel by the Sea. This quaint town is a couple of miles from where I worked. I used to go there all the time to walk and see the coastline with my family.

During some of my off-duty time, I was lucky enough to work security at the "Tour de Elegance" car show at pebble beach. This was a great display of some of the most incredible celebrities and cars in the world. On other weekends when not with my family, I spent time working as a Police Instructor at the local police academy.

***

Life in the Monterey Bay area was great. Fisherman's wharf, the aquarium, the Pacific Grove lantern festival, the beach, and the beautiful Spanish mission in Carmel, so much to do and see for my family and me. Truly one the most beautiful areas of our country.

Things were going great until New Year's Eve.

We set up a New Years Eve DUI Sobriety checkpoint between Salinas and Monterey. Any vehicle that came down the road was directed to the sobriety check.

I was in charge that night, standing back and letting my team run the show. I watched a car full of "gangbangers" pull up in front of me. My sergeant and a patrol officer stood on the driver's side while two officers handled the other side.

After talking to the driver, the sergeant opened all four doors and ordered them to put their hands on the backs of the seats for everyone's safety. While the sergeant dealt with the driver, the officer next to him walked over to the passenger's side. This was a huge mistake.

I watched the two passengers in the back. They were young kids who didn't understand the full ramifications of a life-in-prison sentence.

With their hands on the seat in front of them, it was like slow motion. I saw the kid closest to me take one of his hands off the headrest and reach into a cargo area behind his seat.

248

Instinctively, I jerked my gun from its holster and ran to the car, yelling to the sergeant, "You've got to watch him. He's got something behind the seat." Sure enough, the kid pulled out a handgun, swinging it around at the sergeant.

I yelled, "Gun, Gun, Gun!"

I ran towards the induvial, gun in hand shouting commands. I grabbed his gun hand, while pulling him from the car and down to the ground, contorting my body away from the sergeant so the bullet wouldn't strike his body had it gone off.

This stunned the 14-year-old kid (we later learned his age). To him, I'd come out of nowhere.

I twisted hard before collapsing onto the asphalt. Something had happened that I couldn't explain.

Suddenly, I found myself unable to move from the waist down.

Chapter 17

"If you wanna move up, you gotta move"

I gazed up at the stars, my fellow officers' concerned faces occasionally blocking the view.

"Captain, are you alright?"

The sergeant bent down on one knee and removed the kid's gun from underneath me. Instead of answering him, I thought of Mr. Nebraska, my New York Military Academy football coach.

After each game, he'd approach me and repeat, "Never let go of your guy. And never stop playing until the whistle blows."

Mr. Nebraska was why I'd twisted the gun around, pulling the kid out of the vehicle until I had his hand around my back. I was not giving up. But something happened, and I fell to the asphalt.

What was wrong with me?

"I can't feel anything below my waist," I said.

"We've called an ambulance," Mike said. He was the other Captain. "It'll be here in a sec, and

we'll get you on the bus." (Bus is cop slang for ambulance.)

"Did the gun go off?" I asked.

"No. You kept it from firing."

My mind spun through the possibilities. Fresh Kills. Digging and pulling up girders. The doctors at Mount Sinai Beth Israel Hospital had diagnosed a slipped disc. That had to be it.

"I'm not going out of here in a bus," I said. "Help me up."

"Tony, I've got to get you out of here. You're injured. Just stay still."

"Throw me in the back of the squad car," I said.

Mike frowned. "Are you out of your mind?"

"I don't want my officers to see me leave this street in the back of an ambulance. Get me out of here."

Against all good sense, several officers lifted me up and set me in the back of a patrol car. It was a dumb move on my part.

As Mike pulled away, he urged me to go to the hospital. I talked him out of it.

"Take me home to my wife," I moaned.

He did. Between the two of them, they carried me into the house. Once there, I still couldn't move. I was sure I'd be good as new with a little rest.

I was wrong. The pain was too much. With some help, Amy and Mike loaded me into the car, put Anthony in his child's seat, and took me to the hospital.

After a thorough examination, they said my L-4 disc, normally the size of a marshmallow, had been squished down to the width of a penny. According to the doctors, all the "juice" from the disc had squirted out, which compressed the nerves and essentially left me unable to walk. Surgery was not needed, but I still couldn't walk. It was a scary prognosis.

It took a few weeks before I regained feeling in my legs. Once that happened, it was a couple of months of daily physical therapy. The physical therapists would lower me into a pool using a hoist for water strength exercises. Essentially, they had to teach me how to walk all over again. It took slightly over two months of intense rehabilitation before I could finally return to duty.

But it could've been a whole lot worse. I was very grateful. Those around me didn't know that I was fueled by an intense passion deep inside to keep going and catapulted by the words of that priest during 9/11.

Who would have known this wasn't the end of the obstacles I would face or the lessons I would learn?

***

I worked under Chief Collins for eighteen long months. It was a very satisfying and fulfilling job, but it wasn't where I would lay my hat for any length of time. Although, I always leave a place better than when I came. I touch hearts and lives and improve every environment as I move on to help others. As such, I kept constantly hearing the call to move upward on the promotion ladder. It was a loud call.

I began searching for something back east, closer to our families. Then one day, I received a call from a job application I'd submitted two years earlier. It was an impressive position in Groton, Connecticut. A naval nuclear submarine base was about to be BRAC'd, and they needed a security and law enforcement director.

This was a Directorship, a big step up from Police Captain, and a leap right over the Chief of Police position. They wanted someone with experience going through a BRAC and someone who had already been a police supervisor.

I looked over the particulars. The job paid $20,000 more than I was making, but it required a two-year contract with the option for two more years. Amy and I discussed it. We agreed this opportunity was an opportunity of a lifetime to move up.

The old adage in the government is, "If you wanna move up, you gotta move."

After several interviews, I landed the Director of Security and Law Enforcement job for our nation's first and most historic nuclear submarine base, home of the USS Nautilus, this nation's first nuclear-powered submarine. This was sizing up to be an incredible challenge and patriotic work at its finest. I'd be working for the Department of Navy as a civilian.

With my previous experience in the Air Force Air National Guard and the U.S. Navy Reserves combined with my last job in the Department of the Army, all I needed was to get a job in the Marines. I'd hit the U.S. military "quadfecta." Then again, I was in the Young Marines when I was young; did that count?

253

"Nah, good try," I laughed out loud to myself.

Chief Bill was promoted to Director of Public Safety just as I left. He took the news hard, especially since he'd planned on me becoming the new chief and backfilling for him. "If you get there and don't like it, you come right back. Understand?"

He didn't understand that I'd just signed a two-year contract. I wasn't going anywhere but to Connecticut.

***

As always, Amy and Anthony stayed behind. Amy immediately put in for a transfer, but we knew it would take some time. When you think of a real hero in my story, it would have to be my beautiful wife; she has transferred with me all around the country while sacrificing her opportunity at a promotion, surviving 9/11 standing outside the World Trade Center that very morning, and now leapfrogging back across the country again to follow me. Amy is my hero, hands down. Thank you, honey.

I said goodbye to my family and drove to the Monterey shore. I picked up some sand and held it in my hand. Here I go again, I said to myself. Then, I drove straight to Groton, Connecticut.

Once there, I stepped on the shore, held up some sand, and called my wife.

"I made it!" I told her.

From one coast to the other. What a journey; I "spanned" America as a law enforcement officer; pretty amazing.

"Thank you for all your support!" I said to her.

The next morning, I drove to my new job at the Submarine Base. I pulled into the parking lot and noticed an old building. Walking up to it, I remembered a time when I was younger. I had switched from the Air Force Reserves to the Navy Reserves. Since I didn't need to go back through basic training, they sent me here for orientation.

At the time, I was dating Amy. I had rented a van and brought her along with me to have a long weekend in Connecticut.

I went to the entrance and stood there. What a disaster I experienced in this building. Chuckling, I allowed myself to return to a time long ago…

… Amy and I sat in the van for a moment. "Do you want me to come in with you?" she asked.

"Sure," I replied. "I'm just getting my military-issue uniforms. It shouldn't take long."

We walked inside the uniform shop to find an older lady barely four feet tall.

She looked straight out of Wendy's "Where's the beef?" commercial. Her neck was missing, so her head rested flat on her sagging shoulders. Her head barely moved without her body turning simultaneously in any direction.

"Chit," she said abruptly, holding out her hand, unable to look me in the eyes.

A chit has many meanings in the Navy; it can be a leave slip, a sick leave slip, or a permission slip, and in this case, it was a piece of paper listing the uniforms the Navy wants you to have. I handed it to her as Amy stood by the entrance.

"Cart!" the worker barked. I grabbed one and gazed at the stacks of clothes. The Navy has more uniforms than any other branch of service. It's overwhelming.

"Two of those," she said, pointing.

"One of those."

She didn't even look, instead tossing her finger in the general direction.

I worked fast, grabbing everything I could. By the time we reached the end of a long line, my cart was piled high.

"Take the pants and go in there," she said. "The tailor will take the measurements when you come out."

I took the garments and stepped into the dressing room. Staring at the traditional blue "crackerjacks," I couldn't tell how they went on. Instead, I put on another pair and stepped outside. After the tailor placed his marks, I donned another pair. This continued until I had one pair left: the crackerjacks. It was the moment I dreaded.

I stood alone in the dressing room, turning the blue pants around and around. The Navy was steeped in tradition. And the crackerjack uniform was legendary; its nickname comes from the box of crackerjack popcorn because it's the same uniform depicted on the box. On one side were thirteen gold buttons signifying the original thirteen colonies. A drawstring occupied the opposite side.

Without having gone through the Navy's basic training, I had no idea how to put these pants on. If I put them on wrong, word would get around. I'd never live it down. I had to get this right.

As I held the pants in my hand, I heard the front door open. A tap-tap-tap of shoes belonged to a Navy Chief. I peeked out from behind the curtain and saw the creature. He was terrifying—tall and barrel-chested. His sleeve was covered with rank, which made him a master chief petty officer or E9, the highest rank a noncommissioned seaman could achieve. He had his war face on and was coming straight toward me.

I closed the curtain. This monster had to be the one who would put me through the orientation. Suddenly, beads of sweat popped out all over my face and neck. I studied the crackerjacks again, desperately trying to get my brain to work.

Come on, Tony, use some logic.

There was no way the Navy would allow us to sit on thirteen gold buttons. I suddenly remembered an episode from the Little Rascals comedy show. In the episode, I remembered the rascal having to use the restroom and opening the trap door. In this case, the 13-button trap door. The light went on! I said, I got it; they had to go in the rear. The drawstring was useless in the rear. After all, how the heck could you tie a drawstring from behind? "Nah, I got this bad boy," I thought.

I was certain this was the right way; how else would I go to the bathroom if the buttons were in the front? I mean, if all those buttons were up front, how would I take a leak? No way. The buttons, once undone, would create a large loose flap. If I had to go number two, I'd need that much room in the back. It would make much more sense if the drawstring were upfront; hey, it worked for the Little Rascals. Yep! That was it—buttons in the back and drawstring upfront.

I stepped out of the dressing room, sweat pouring from my body. The tailor was there, stunned.

"Oh my god, Oh my God, what have you done!" the old lady screamed.

"They're backward!"

The master chief petty officer took one look, put his hands on his hips, and blew a gasket. The scene reminded me of those cartoons where the angry buffalo has steam coming out of its ears and nostrils.

"Did you just join my United States Navy?" the master chief petty officer said through clenched jaws.

"Yes, sir," I eked out.

"What's happening to us?" he yelled. "I'd better get out of here before...." He didn't finish the sentence. Instead, he pounded a fist into his palm.

Near the front door, Amy was bent over laughing. The "Where's the beef" lady joined Amy in laughter, literally doubled over. Two guys who had come in after me listened as the old lady detailed my stupidity. It was a horrendous welcome to the Navy.

I never trusted the Little Rascals again. Thankfully, I survived...

Funny as it would seem, I never had to wear that uniform the entire time I served. Go figure, all that for nothing.

… I looked over the old building. It was now a lawn and garden storage center—just lawnmowers and fertilizer. At least I could button up that chapter of my life.

"Excuse me, sir, are you the new director of security?"

I turned around and saw a petty officer coming toward me. "Yes, I am."

"Okay, I'm your courtesy escort. Why didn't you park in the spot with the director's sign?"

"Satellites, my friend, someone's always watching; no need for the enemy to know they just hired a new security director?"

"Yes, sir."

"Let's not make it easy for them."

The petty officer gave a crooked grin. "Oh, I see."

"Take me on a tour," I said. "I want to check the place out."

The base occupied a lot of acreage. It was famous for being the first nuclear submarine facility in the United States—the USS Nautilus was docked there, our nation's first nuclear-powered submarine. The base also serviced the hunter-killer subs—the ones that crept off silently, looking for other subs to kill in case of war.

During the day, the base was very active. The Subs and the submariner's school were the primary focus of the base's mission. Sailors who served on submarines learned their new chosen way of life at the Sub School, as it was called. Several residential buildings were on-site, and everything else was needed to service and train submariners.

Reducing crime, safeguarding the facility and those who work and visit, and protecting the subs and the sailors were the main priorities of my new job. I supervised law enforcement; these were Department of the Navy civilian police officers who patrolled the installation, traffic court (we wrote tickets to violators) and operated a full administrative traffic court, risk management, anti-terrorism, vehicle and delivery inspections, a guard contract for our security officers, a police and security boat division, a complete K9 unit with dozens of dogs, and all the physical security and emergency management for the base.

To accomplish that, I had a large cadre of military personnel under my charge combined with all the other programs. I supervised a boat division to patrol the Thames River and surrounding coastline for those attempting to gather intelligence information on base activities and potential intruders. And it was all my responsibility. All this was now under my leadership from the guy who once put his pants on backward; I had to laugh at myself. But at the same time, they are immensely driven and proud about protecting those who defend America.

At the start of our tour, I couldn't tell the front entrance from a wall. There needed to be signage to direct people to the main office. This was a problem. I had sold the men who'd hired me on bringing in some serious customer service. You can't help people if they can't find you.

When the tour was over, I released the petty officer and walked back to what I thought was the main entrance. The door was locked. I tried another. It was secured. Door after door wouldn't open.

I pulled out my cell phone and called the petty officer who dropped me off. "These doors are all locked, and you didn't give me any keys. Can you please bring them over?" This was a red flag, as we say in the government; in essence, it's a sign of impending and larger issues behind the scenes.

The petty officer handed me a ring of three keys. Three keys for an entire nuclear submarine base? Something was wrong here. Very wrong.

I took off on my own and laid hands on every wall and door in each building. One door would not open with any of the three keys. I called the escort, who told me he didn't have it. I needed to climb over his head.

I located active-duty Navy Lt. Joe Manard, the man responsible for working with me on security as my new deputy.

"I need the keys to this door," I told him as we stood before it. "I'd like to know what's behind this door."

"That's just storage, sir," he said calmly. "You don't have to worry about it."

"But I'd like to see what's behind the door," I firmly insisted.

"We'll have to find the key and get it to you."

At the end of the day, I watched him climb into his car and drive home. The message I received from this act was straightforward: "I will decide when you get the keys."

I smirked. He was hiding something.

A few minutes later, I located the senior enlisted officer right below the lieutenant. Sure enough, he knew where all the keys were located and was happy to help me.

We walked to the mystery door and tried several of them. "You sure you want to look in there?" he asked me.

"What are you guys hiding in this room?"

Finally, he unlocked the door. Before he could fully open it, the door slammed into my body as gear poured out. I stepped back and watched it all hit the floor. I'd never seen anything like it. It was like a can I opened once. A fake snake sprung out, scaring the "blank" out of me. Instead of a spring-loaded snake, it was rubber gloves, Gore-Tex jackets, hats, shoes, and military clothes. I peeked inside. The room was huge.

"What is all this?" I asked the officer.

"Why would you push this equipment up against the door? And why is it not organized?"

He put his hands in his pockets and glanced around. "I don't know if I should tell you the story."

I got in his face. "You'd better tell me the story. I'm directing you to tell me. What is all this stuff?"

He quickly spilled the beans. The previous year, a deputy had ordered this wet- and cold-weather gear from a vendor in China. When it arrived, everything was two sizes smaller than U.S. sizes.

The person ordering didn't account for the difference in sizes. He didn't tell anybody about it either. He just locked everything in this room and tried to hide it, thinking he might retire and leave it for the next guy.

Well, I was the next guy.

This stuff added up to over $100,000. I had to report it to the base inspector general. No way I was taking the fall for this screwup.

Needless to say, I sat the leadership team down and told them, "No more secrets." If we were to make this the best security directorate in the Navy, we would have to work together. Honesty was the ingredient that would make us true to the mission.

***

The Navy put me in the base hotel shortly after I arrived. Like my last job, I had a short walk to the office.

My first order of business was to renovate the Department. Yet I had to be fiscally wise since the base would be shut down in two to four years.

First, I sent the mystery room gear to several other bases with sailors who fit it. A handful of phone calls were taken care of. Then, I took over the mystery room for our new training department. They were ecstatic; when I arrived, they were operating out of a coat closet—something about closets at this place.

Next, I obtained permission from the base Captain to use the entire wing of that same building (previously used by the Brigg, the naval correctional center) to expand our training section further and provide indoor training rooms. Training is key to having the most responsive, best-trained troops. Which ultimately converts to lives saved and assets protected.

With that done, I ordered signage to direct folks to our building. Working through the Navy's construction department, we reorganized the security department quickly for very little money. I leveraged existing resources.

I met with the traffic court judge, the contract suitability unit, fleet utilization, and the anti-terrorism units, and they all checked out well. So, I left it alone. I firmly believe that if it's not broken, don't fix it.

Although, with the flurry of activity, it didn't take long to receive my first big caper. When I was onboarded through human resources, I was commissioned as the Installation "Command Investigator." My role in this unique capacity was investigating crime and sensitive violations on or around the installation. I reported on these matters to the Inspector General and the Installation Commander.

This particular case involved theft. At the end of a four-month tour underwater with no daylight, the sailors were released to the base with lots of time off and even more money to spend. For young men, this could have been a better combination.

One day, a boat surfaced and docked, releasing the sailors. The single ones ran to their ten-story building apartments on the base. They were usually with everyone in the same boat.

While they were gone, a trustworthy sailor was put in charge. He was called C.Q. or Charge of Quarters. The C.Q. sat at the entrance and greeted the sailors when they returned, ensuring no one came in who wasn't supposed to be there.

On this occasion, several sailors reached their apartments only to find their belongings gone. The skipper of the boat was noticeably upset. He had been out to sea protecting his men only to learn they had not been protected onshore. The sailors were furious too. Everyone wanted the culprit strung up from a yardarm.

It didn't take a genius to come up with the prime suspect. I could've solved this caper in a few weeks as a manager. But being in management means delegating. Otherwise, you're not managing. You're doing. I was too consumed with the changes I made in the Department and wanted to show significant improvement to the base Captain.

So, I turned to my list of detectives; I had both military and civilian detectives. I pulled out my list. At the top was Seamus Collins.

Seamus Collins was a U.S. Navy master at arms (a military policeman, in military-speak). He claimed to be a direct descendent of Michael Collins from Ireland—a revolutionary and politician in the Irish War of Independence in the early 1900s.

Seamus stood six feet four inches tall and looked like Liam Neeson, the lead in the movie Michael Collins—a perfect choice to lead this case.

I put Seamus on the case right away. It took him only a short time; he was used to working cases like this from his time in the Navy, especially overseas. He had a suspect in about two weeks, faster than I had imagined myself doing it.

The prime suspect turned out to be a civilian, the maintenance man, which is why the C.Q. never suspected anything. The maintenance man would load up items (after using his master key to enter rooms) in his trash container and then out the back door to his car. No one suspected a thing, not even the local pawn shop, who was very happy with the business.

There's nothing worse in the Navy world than theft, nothing; It's not tolerated at all.

He was on vacation that particular week, so Seamus put together a case against him while he was gone. All we had to do was wait until he returned.

***

A week later, he returned. However, Seamus and I were off duty that day. By the time we showed up for work Monday morning, we had another crime to solve, credit card theft.

When sailors climbed onboard a sub, they handed over their credit cards, licenses, and passports to the Captain. All of which are locked in an onboard safe. This was done because, occasionally, a sub might surface in another country. If the sailors were given shore leave, they needed their credit cards and I.D.s to get around. Usually, though, the sub stayed underwater, so the cards remained untouched in the safe. Let's face it; the other reason was to keep honest people honest.

This time, as always, the sailors were handed their wallets as they left the sub. Most of them weren't going to check the contents. They'd do that when they got to their apartment.

However, we soon received a report that two wallets were missing, and one had all the cash removed.

After some brief questioning, Seamus and I learned that the bursar was the only person on board with access to the safe during that cruise. We quickly found our culprit. He received a court martial and severe discipline.

Now we returned to the civilian employee suspected of taking the sailors' belongings. A firm line of questioning followed up with some camera footage sealed his fate. He was later charged and terminated.

After all the excitement, the next day was the grand opening of the new customer service department for my directorate. I had worked tirelessly since the first day of not being able to determine which door was the entrance to the building and vowed to deliver a better department for the subbase community. One that served the community, not the other way around.

I started the process by establishing a new main entrance and then creating a new customer service department. Then, I assigned a team leader to spearhead the work. Everyone chipped in, new carpet, painting, new pictures, repurposed furniture from other buildings, and even a new coffee maker. It was a complete success and caused everyone to bond. Collectively working towards a common goal does that.

Then I dedicated this section to the sailors who died on the U.S.S Cole, some of which worked at our Department, and invited their families to join us in the grand opening. It was a beautiful day. The local news covered the celebration, and the event boosted the morale of the Department and base.

The department "gelled" after that; we really took off morale-wise and workwise. The employees loved the renovations and the huge new training department. After that, I reorganized the various sections within the organization to fit into the new strategic plan; the "re-org" made it more effective and efficient. I made sure to integrate the active-duty military personnel with the civilian personnel so they could complement each other's work. Everything was making sense.

I enjoyed an incredible experience working for the submarine base. Our work led the base to be kept open and the community enriched.

It almost goes without saying, though, just like the civilian world, we have our share of problems and issues that arise in the military and must be dealt with swiftly, and we do. However, our Navy and other branches of service are steeped in honor, tradition, and hard-driving, dedicated service members who work tirelessly to defend our nation. Trust me; I was one, so I know firsthand. I was very proud to have served as a sailor and as a Director.

Chapter 18

Chief of Police, Hoover Dam

That being said, I was still a civilian and I was coming up on my two years at the Base. With only a few short months left of my age, I was notified by our Human Resources department that I had a limited time left to jump back into the government's special law enforcement retirement system.

Francis Johnston, the head of human resources on the Navy base, called, "Tony, you do realize time is ticking, and the window will soon close for you to get back into the special retirement. Let me know if you want to leave and seek a position that will honor the previous years you put into the retirement?" she said.

It's complicated, but basically, there are two types of retirement in federal service, a standard administrative retirement and a special retirement for law enforcement and firefighters. I jumped out of the special retirement when I took the Directors' job at subbase primarily because they didn't offer it for that level of position. I liked the dynamics of the job, so I took it, but it came with a price of leaving the special retirement.

So, I knew how valuable it was and started looking for a new position that offered special retirement. This meant having to leave the submarine base.

I began my quest looking for a law enforcement position that would carry this retirement, and I eventually found one.

Chief of Police for the Hoover Dam.

The Hoover Dam fell under the US Department of the Interior, Bureau of Reclamation, and the position was located in Boulder City, Nevada, a short distance from downtown Las Vegas.

I thought, "This would be an incredible opportunity to protect a national icon" Wow, the thought of it came with the "wow" effect.

This was taking my craft to a whole new level. Although protecting our nation's first nuclear submarine base wasn't bad either, let's admit, protecting nuclear submarines was pretty cool.

Although this job was not only protecting one of the seven wonders of the world. It was also a functioning water distribution facility and power generation plant. Hoover Dam delivers power to over nine power and water customers south of the dam. Having the reigns of security for this Icon was equally as serious.

I submitted my application for the position. A few weeks after the announcement closed, I received word I was selected for a telephone interview. They were moving fast on filling this job.

I did well on the telephonic interview consisting of a six-person panel. Then I sweated it out for a couple days afterward. By the end of the week, I received another call. This time it was from human resources.

"Mr. Losito, we're holding interviews all next week, and you've been selected to come to the Hoover Dam Regional Office in Boulder City, Nevada, for a formal in-person interview; you made it to the next phase; congratulations, sir!" Diane said.

I took a deep breath; I knew the clock was ticking on the window for me to get back in. I booked a train from Connecticut to Las Vegas. Yup, a train; I don't like to fly. How long, you ask? It took about two days in total with all the switching. Hey, it's my way of traveling; think of it, you get to see America; it's like an 8th-grade history class field trip. You meet the cross-section of America on the train you would never otherwise meet fascinating people.

I made it to the interview. The chair of the panel was a retired NYPD Police Captain. Needless to say, we hit it off very well, and I aced the interview. I think the clincher was when the chairperson, Peter, asked me, "So Tony if you had problems on your back shift, how would you handle it?"

"You mean the midnight to eight shift?"

"Yeah, you work during the day, and issues could potentially occur on the midnight shift, so how would you address those issues?"

"Well, I would speak to the supervisor of the shift."

"How? He works midnights, and you come on in the morning after he has already gone home?"

"Ahh, well, I wouldn't speak to him after he's gone home; I would go to the roll call at the start of the shift, introduce myself to the midnight team, who probably hasn't seen a Chief show up in years, and afterward I would visit with the supervisor to diagnose what's occurring."

"Perfect," he said, "That's the answer we were looking for."

I suspected the previous applicant didn't figure that one out, and the panel had laid a bet that I would.

By the time I got back to Connecticut, I was hired, and it was off to Nevada. I recall Amy just placing her hand over her forehead, "Okay, can you please tell me where we are going now?"

"The Hoover Dam, dear, we're gonna make history; we've got a national icon to protect, let's start packing.

***

It was December of 2007 when I landed in Las Vegas.

"Don't ever bring my kids here!" Amy said as we took the drive up the Las Vegas strip for her first time.

"This is not a place to raise our children; I don't want them to ever come here." I thought for sure there was no way out of this one. She wasn't sold on the glitz and glitter. My plan was after we arrived in town to take her to the Las Vegas Strip and wow her with the magic of Vegas, but it backfired on me.

I quickly cut the Strip tour short and took her to the hotel. The government put us up for the next 45 days until our things arrived, and we could house hunt for a permanent home. Thankfully the hotel was on the outskirts of Vegas in the suburb of Henderson. For the most part, it was a quiet bedroom community.

We soon found a lovely two-bedroom house to rent. That gave us the next year to scout the area and determine where we wanted to purchase a home.

In the meantime, I got acclimated to my new position.

Now, the Hoover Dam is considered by some to be the eighth wonder of the world. It's been designated as a national icon aside from being a functioning hydroelectric power and water generation facility delivering power and water to Arizona, California, and even Mexico.

Construction of the dam began in 1931 and was completed in 1936, oddly enough during the Great Depression.

The structure is made of concrete and is an arch-gravity-type dam. It's built on the Colorado River within the Black Canyon and sits smack dab in the middle of the state line for both Nevada and Arizona.

During daylight savings time, one side is an hour ahead timewise than the other.

I must say, it was truly an honor to have been selected to serve my country for a national icon. The effort it took to build the dam, the lives that were lost in its construction, and the sheer pride in which it represents to our nation had me personally swelling with pride. Now being in charge of the safety and security of this great testament to our nation's history was truly amazing.

Shortly after arriving, I took my first ride down to the dam from the police station. The station was situated about a half mile up the road from the dam. I stood by the winged arch monument at the top of the dam and eventually walked over to the edge of the downstream wall and took it all in.

The location for so many iconic movies such as "Viva Las Vegas" with Elvis Presley, "Fools Rush In" starring Matthew Perry and

Salma Hayek, "Vegas Vacation" with Chevy Chase, and the "Transformers" to name a few.

Breathtaking and utterly magnificent, the structure of the mountains, the air. The magnitude of it all was captivating and left me in awe.

After I had my moment, it was time to get rolling. I held my first staff meeting and began to assess the program. I quickly evaluated the commanders and determined who would be assigned to what job to support the direction we truly needed to go.

No sooner did my first meeting come to an end than my new administrative assistant Carlos came to my office. "Sir, it's the Deputy Director of the Dam; he has asked you to meet him for lunch today. He said to meet him at the Hoover Dam café, Nevada side."

"Okay, please let him know I will be down shortly."

The Hoover Dam had two cafés, one on the Nevada side and one on the Arizona side. The food was okay, the lunch menu, really.

I met Tim, the Deputy Director, for lunch. He ordered two Chef salads and bought me lunch. As we found a quiet table in the corner away from the tourists, he said, "Tony, here's the keys to the main police facility, the boat launch station, and the elevator at the topside of the dam that goes to the administrative offices below, this should be everything you need."

"Excuse me?" I said.

"Everything I need?", "What do you mean?"

"Yes, this should basically provide you access to the areas you need to get to; your officers have keys to everywhere else, and we are open 24/7, so everything else is accessible."

"Ahh, Tim, what about regular meetings with you and the Director regarding funding, staffing, vehicles, and coordination of the department and activities here at the dam?"

He said, "Tony, listen, I am an engineer, the Director is an engineer, we don't know anything about running a police department or security of critical infrastructure, you do, that's why we hired you. Call us if you run into a jam; we will send funding as you need it."

He got up, shook my hand, and said have a great day, and proceeded back to his office at the base of the dam.

I felt empty with a rattled combination of shock and awe. Nothing like being handed the keys to a police department for a national icon and told to figure it out. I was left standing there in my new crisp, clean blue police uniform, looking like General Patton with four stars on my collar but much different than he ever appeared in photos, with a very unsure look on my face like someone had just hit me in the head with a wet squirrel.

What just happened? I asked myself. Did I just get set up for failure, or was this guy really serious?

I'd soon find out.

Chapter 19

"Code Red!"

I returned to the station, still scratching my head, but I needed to look confident in front of the troops. The best leaders always know what to do. Hell, you need to always be prepared mentally for anything to pop off at a moment's notice, and low and behold, it did.

No sooner than I emerged from using the men's room, my first Lieutenant came running up to me shouting, "Chief, Chief, we have a Code Red! A Code Red!"

I immediately pulled myself together from bathroom mode to emergency mode. I told the Lieutenant to go, and I would jump in a separate squad car and follow.

A Code Red was when a person or persons ran through our security checkpoint in their vehicle without stopping and with intent. They usually did this at a high rate of speed either to potentially attack the Dam, hurt others by using their car as a weapon, or they may have been fleeing a crime in nearby Las Vegas. On other occasions, their intent was to commit suicide, either by jumping off the Dam or "suicide by cop" with my officers.

Code Reds were serious, as serious as it gets.

Code Reds are literally an all-hands-on-deck alert. At any given moment, thousands of tourists are peppered on and around the Dam, and dozens of employees and contractors are working about.

Despite the fact, the Dam is a functioning water and power generation facility. We couldn't afford a potential terrorist attack, crime, or undesirable event to take place.

That's why we originally established security checkpoints in both Arizona and Nevada. You were required to be inspected before anyone could drive on, across, or down to the Dam to visit.

Everyone went to their battle stations.

I grabbed a police unit and headed down to the "S" curve, as we called it, just before the narrow stretch north of the visitor's center. We deployed our pop-up barriers in the event the vehicle didn't stop. These are vehicle safety crash barriers that rise instantly up out of the roadway that will instantly stop a moving vehicle or truck.

As I arrived at the top of the "S" curve, my Sergeant had the suspect vehicle stopped, and the driver at gunpoint. A combination of officers with automatic rifles and handguns were employed to ensure the driver fully understood he was to stop his vehicle and not proceed any further. Dozens of tourists were all around.

In this instance, a man in his 60s driving a late model sedan station wagon fully loaded with personal effects had "blown" the Nevada security checkpoint for reasons unknown to us at the time.

My Sergeant commanded the driver to place his vehicle in "park" and turn off the ignition. Then to place his hands out the window. Thankfully he complied if he had not, the implications would have been grave.

I walked down to the vehicle, my weapon drawn as well, carefully approaching the rear of the vehicle, and watching for potential crossfire with my officers.

I could see piles of materials strew throughout the vehicle in what looked like he was living out of his car. Kind of like a hoarder would live.

As the Sergeant directed another officer to move closer toward the driver to attempt to secure him, I could see dozens and dozens of tourists now gathered around like it was a scene from a movie. I ordered the other responding officers south of the event over my radio to move the tourists back for their safety.

"Have two units draw tape and cordon off the area and move the tourist back," I said.

Dispatch: "Hoover 1, Hoover 1, Chief, are we secure?"

"No, I answered, the subject is not yet secured, we are still active, the scene is live, I repeat, we are not code 4, standby", I said.

As the officer responsible for securing the driver moved in, I could hear the Sergeant, who was serving as one of the cover officers positioned on the passenger side near the front, suddenly shout,

"Gun, Gun, there's a sawed-off shotgun on the front seat right next to him."

I then echoed the Sergeant's commands for everyone around me to hear. *The* stakes just rose considerably.

The Sergeant motions to the officer, moving in to secure the subject. The Sergeant kept a cat's eye view on the driver and the shotgun.

The officer shouts while holding the driver at gunpoint, "Driver, Driver, keep your eyes on me, follow my commands, keep your hands out the window, and don't move until I tell you to do so.

Do you understand me?"

"Yes, I do," said the driver.

Another cover officer creeps up from behind, then the officer issuing commands. The arresting officer moves in and places handcuffs on the suspect while simultaneously removing him from the car and placing him prone on the ground.

The Sergeant swiftly moves into the front seat and secures the shotgun.

"Dispatch, Dispatch, we are code 4, all secure at this time, no other occupants, and the subject is in custody", I said.

My officers had crushed it and done a superb job keeping visitors and Dam safe.

Following an hour-long interview and search of the subject's vehicle, he admitted he ran the security checkpoint point because he was tired of taking all the medicine his doctors put him on for anxiety and wanted to commit suicide. He told us that he would've aimed his weapon at the police had they tried to prevent him from killing himself on top of the Dam.

It was a close call by any measure and only moments after I had arrived at the job.

I thought *it was such a beautiful place; I would never have imagined this kind of thing would occur here.*

Boy, was I in for a rude awakening?

***

"The windows don't open in hotels on the Vegas strip," my deputy informed me.

"So, if you think today's event was interesting, just give it a week."

Well, he couldn't be any more right. Almost to the day, a week later, I received a call at 2:30am.

"Chief, we're gonna need you to come in; it's a suicide, downstream side of the dam," my command center leader said.

"Okay, I will be right there; give me about 20 Mikes." Mikes are minutes in cop-speak.

I jumped into "5 Star", my Lemans blue C-5 Corvette with a license plate that read "five-star," and sped off to the Dam from my home in Henderson. Hey, I had five stars on the collar, so I had to do the license plate.

Listen, if you're gonna do a job like this, the least you can do is have a cool car with a cool vanity plate! It makes dealing with everything that much easier on the ride home.

When I arrived, there was a green SUV parked at the top of the Dam, the driver's side door was open, with one of my officers looking over the downstream side of the Dam. The downstream side is the refence we use to describe the downriver (from the reservoir) side or front face of the Dam.

It's about a 736-foot drop to the roof of the federal administrative offices situated at the front face of the Dam.

I said to the officer, "What do we have?"

He said, "It appears to be a female around 40-something years old. We already reviewed the video footage from the command center. She appeared to park her Jeep here at the top of the Dam, climbed on the safety wall, stood up, made the sign of the cross, put her arms out to the side as if she was forming wings of a plane, and proceeded to dive off. She landed on the roof of the administrative offices below Chief."

"Who do we have down there?"

"The shift lieutenant and a foreman from facilities who helped him gain access."

"Okay, what side is she on?"

"Nevada, Sir"

"Alright, let's call the Las Vegas coroner's office and get them out here."

"Yes, sir, we're on it."

It turns out she was married and had a family. We were never really certain why she chose to do what she did, but she was part of a long list of unfortunate souls who would take their lives at the Hoover Dam.

Most were associated with gambling, losing their life's savings in the glitz and glimmer of the Las Vegas strip.

That's why the windows don't open on Vegas high-rise hotels.

Over my three and a half years serving as Chief of Police, we would encounter approximately 22 individuals a year who either attempted to commit suicide or committed suicide. It was the side of Vegas most never saw or talked about.

In between all that, over the years, we dealt with everything from snake calls, parking disputes, and people stealing rocks from the site, which they would later sell as Hoover Dam souvenirs, (Taking anything from the environment is against the law on Reclamation land, to include rocks or vegetation), on to assaults, thefts at the gift shops, individuals who attempted to bring weapons on tours, medical calls, (most for heat exhaustion), and even ghost calls.

Yup, Ghost calls at the Hoover Dam.

By the end of my first 10 months, we received a call from a tourist who claimed to see the Ghost of the Hoover Dam mascot dog, "Nig."

Known to workers who built the Dam in the early 1930s as "nobody's dog and everybody's dog," Nig was a stray born in Boulder City, where the workers of the Dam were housing during the construction. Nig was brought by the Chief Engineer one day to the worksite, and he quickly became a mascot to the workers, raising morale everywhere he went. A statue now exists of Nig at the top of the Dam.

One evening as the sun was setting, around twilight time, a tourist called the police dispatch. She stated that she'd just seen a ghostly dog run right past the Nig statue and later disappear into the rock wall sever yards away. My officers responded, but of course, there was nothing to be found other than the statue, and he wasn't moving.

Ghost sightings at the Dam were not out of the norm. My officers would tell me they would see the Ghost of the lift operator in the old lift house. This was the small building used to operate the cable lift that once carried supplies to the Dam. Officers claimed to have seen the operator. Other officers and tourists claimed to have seen "sightings" of the "high scalers." During the construction of the Dam, these men (called High Scalers) climbed down the canyon walls on ropes. They operated jackhammers to strip away loose rock to form the canyon.

It's hard not to imagine, with all the lives lost during the time the Dam was built and those who poured their hearts into its construction, that there wouldn't be residual energy still at the Dam.

Like an old movie, they were simply replaying their roles.

***

Not long after rolling off the ghost dog call, we received a "Bolo" or "Be on the Lookout."

This is a police term used by law enforcement agencies to notify other agencies when they would like us to be aware and on the lookout concerning a wanted suspect or a person of interest from their jurisdiction.

It can also be used to notify other agencies of a missing person or persons. Sort of like the good old days in the movies when they called it an "APB" or all-points bulletin. It was usually information put out for us to be on alert of suspects on the loose. Most always, they were armed and dangerous.

This particular BOLO was for two teenage suspects that had just killed an elderly couple. Turns out the couple were the parents of one of the suspects.

The two had decided to flee south to Arizona. The fastest route from the Las Vegas area to Arizona was across the Hoover Dam.

Little did we know it, but by the time we received the BOLO, the pair had already crossed the Dam and were in Arizona, making their way through a remote stretch of desert just after the Dam. Unbeknownst to us, they changed their mind several hours later. By dawn, they were headed back in our direction.

Fortunately, we always had an officer posted on the Arizona side of the Hoover Dam. This officer was to address issues that occurred strictly in Arizona, a large coverage area of around 11 square miles. The Dam sits smack dab in the middle of Arizona and Nevada, right on the state line.

When the suspects arrived at the Dam, it was around sunrise, and they decided to stop, park, and climb over the guardrails toward the rocky cliffs just above the Dam's upstream side. This was a few hundred feet drop had they fallen. One of the suspects appeared to be contemplating suicide, as this was a suicide hotspot.

As a matter of act, an older man just the week prior had parked his truck there and left a note for police to find. He left a letter addressed to his son along with $500.00 in cash just before he leaped to his death. He drove the night before from Utah because his son was living in Vegas. It was a sad sorry, as his wife had died a year earlier and after his son moved away, he became too lonely to continue.

Our Arizona officer quickly noticed them as they reached the Dam. He matched the car model and license plate to the vehicle the suspects were driving through the description in the BOLO.

He knew right away we had the right suspects. He called for assistance then without hesitation rushed to one suspect who appeared to be contemplating jumping off the edge of the rock adjacent to the Dam. This was a huge cliff face. The officer ordered him to stop. He complied.

Both immediately raised their hands and were placed under arrest. Everyone was safe, and the suspects were in custody.

Then it wasn't long before I found myself on the evening news describing how we'd apprehended the suspects. Fine work by our officers, but truly a tragic day for the parents of one suspect; another set of teenage lives lost.

***

Soon after I arrived, I began working to bring morale up in the department by making a litany of solid changes. I started with families, getting everyone together, unity. When Friday nights rolled around, I reserved it as family night. Each Friday night, the leaders and officers would select a different restaurant on the Las Vegas strip to get together with our families. It was a blast. There were so many restaurants on the strip you could go out every Friday for ten years and never go to the same one twice.

Saturdays were golf days, and Saturday nights were for the wives. We'd all go to concerts or shows. The idea worked, and before long, we were a very tight-knit group. We worked hard, and we played hard, but we always stuck together. If anyone experienced an issue, personal or otherwise, we took care of each other.

The more we bonded as a team, so did the improvements continue. I went on to redecorate the police station, built a SWAT team, created a rope rescue team, along with a backcountry rescue team, created new patches, new patrol cars with a whole new graphic design, a website (the first ever police department page), and hired the first-ever K-9 Dog and handler at the Hoover Dam. Totally modernizing the department front to back.

I even allowed tattoos to be shown after officers had been told to wear long sleeves to cover them up in the 110-degree heat for the past ten years. The previous Chief was a bit old-fashioned and didn't like them.

I went on to hire the first two female officers in over five years. The department hadn't employed any female officers, not good. Diversity is what makes the environment flourish. It is what makes America Flourish.

I went on to build a new firearms range at the Hoover Dam, commissioned the first-ever Hoover Dam patrol boat, and purchased segways and ATVs (all-terrain vehicles) to help with off-road emergencies.

Lastly, I painted the outside of the building with a new coat of paint and fixed the Police Sign so the "C" in the police was now lit after several years. I built a new break area for the officers, created new ranks and jobs, and obtained vital training in hostage negotiation and death investigations for our officers.

I then developed a new position that we had never had in the department. Strangely enough, you would have thought it would have already existed, but it didn't.

On Friday morning, before we were all looking forward that evening to heading to dinner with our families; I took a smoke break out behind the station.

A great man once said to me (his name was James Browne, my father-in-law and a former US Navy officer and airline executive) that *"Tobacco has helped me through some of the hardest times of my life, but don't abuse it, and stop once the hard times are over."*

Well, I had taken to enjoying pipe smoking while serving in my role. I thoroughly enjoyed it and collected several pipes, which helped me through some tough times.

This one particular morning, I stepped out behind the station. The sun was already out; it was a nice morning and a perfect day outside. The Vegas Area has about 360-plus days of sunshine, so the odds you're gonna have a good day are pretty good!

All my officers were on patrol, and my deputy was at a meeting.

As I looked around, I was continually amazed at the landscape and the animals native to the area. Remember, I was born and raised in New York City; the desert was not a place I was all that familiar with, despite having already been around the country.

I looked up and could see big horn sheep dotting the mountainside just east of the station. Amazing animals, so beautiful, so powerful.

Then I looked down and saw a tarantula scurry into its hole by the edge of the building. They move with strikingly fast speed. First time I'd ever seen one.

However, my enchanting little wild kingdom moment would quickly turn sideways, as we say in law enforcement jargon when something goes bad quickly.

Things were about to really go sideways.

Chapter 20

Police Chief Magazine

As the tarantula finally made its way back to his hole, I heard what sounded like a rattle. Now, you've gotta understand this. I am from New York -check, never lived in the dessert-check, went to the zoo, ewh, yeah, a few times-check. But I've only heard that sound twice in my life, once while watching cartoons as a kid and the other time s during a nature show.

I slowly turned to my right, carefully and ever so gracefully, with that sheer sense and expectation that something bad was waiting. You know, like a "jump scare" from a spooky movie.

Yup, you guessed it, a rattlesnake right there at my feet, about a yard from where I was standing.

Really, I thought, after everything I'd been through, it was all going to end with me being bitten by a rattlesnake, and there wasn't a sole around to see it or help me.

Sewer rats, junkyard dogs, organized crime, people high on drugs, poop in elevators, I could deal with all that; heck, I grew up in that world. But rattlesnakes are not good, no matter what time of day. Not huh, not my forte.

I was not familiar with how to handle a rattlesnake. Then again, I wasn't going to stand there and let myself get bitten, either. I slowly started to move backward, inching ever so carefully. Then I drew my weapon.

I pointed it at the snake as if he was a suspect who was armed and dangerous and just robbed a bank.

No, I wasn't even sure I'd hit him should I have taken a shot. But I had to defend myself, I thought. I wasn't a snake wrangler, so my weapon was the only immediate option that came to mind.

Once I was safely far enough back at the corner of the building, my next concern was how I was going to get this snake away from the building so my officers didn't run into it and get bitten.

Then the light went on, and I remembered watching shark week the night prior; thank God for shark week. On the show, they explained how sharks eat almost anything, from other fish to license plates and even people.

That was it, the "ah ha" moment. Suddenly the thousands of dollars the government spent on my training; it was shark week that would serve as the training to guide me through this.

The way I figured was if these ferocious animals eat anything, then a snake, equally ferocious, would as well.

The officers held a barbecue a few days prior to celebrate another officer who was leaving, so we had some hot dogs left over in the freezer.

Hot dogs are cylindrical, the shape of a rattlesnake's body, so it makes sense that it would be a perfect fit to help lure the snake away. They have to go down easy I thought.

"Great idea', I'll get the dogs."

I re-holstered and headed back into the building with breakneck speed. I grabbed a couple of frozen hot dogs from the department freezer and headed back out.

Yup, he's still there, as if he knew I purposefully went back to get something for him to eat. The fact he waited made me even more encouraged that the plan would work.

I crept slowly towards him, one hand holding the hot dog and the other holding my gun. A sight to be seen. An armed hot dog cop.

I figured the snake needed a whiff of the hot dog before I tossed it over to the left where there was dirt hill. The idea was to lead or lure him to the dirt hill, and then he would slitter away pursuing the hotdog.

Like if I was feeding my dog, I said, "Here, little snake, get a whiff of this, looks good right?"

"Hummm, tasty, right?"

Letting him get a good whiff.

I tossed it over in the dirt just on the edge of the parking area. It landed right where the asphalt meets the dirt.

Hmm, it didn't seem to work, but no problem, I am loaded with a backup hot dog, I grabbed two, smart.

So, I give it another try.

"Here, little rattlesnake, here, boy," just like I do with my dog."

"Nothing."

"He ain't going for it."

A light suddenly goes on in my head; I need to heat them up. No wonder he isn't going for it; it's frozen, and he can't smell it. Light goes on in my head. Frozen food doesn't have any odor.

So, I ran back in, secretly hoping he would wait because I really wanted to test this new theory. I heat up a hot dog in the microwave and dash back out. Strangely enough, at this point, I don't want him to leave.

Thank goodness he's still there. Ironically though, it would've been better if he'd left, then waited around for me to warm up the hot dog. Ahh, heck, I am just glad he waited.

I took the "warmed-up" hot dog and proceeded to taunt him a third time.

"Okay, Mr. Snake, now this is much more appetizing, isn't it. A nice warm hot dog, and it should fit very nicely. Here you go, now slither away up the hill", as I gently toss the third hot dog over to the now-growing pile of frozen hot dogs.

Nothing again; he is still rattling and not moving. At this point, I've run out of options. The cat is out of the bag; this is the one thing the Chief knows nothing about. Time to call in an expert.

I call the dayshift sergeant. In law enforcement, sergeants always know what to do. I called Sergeant Sam Petro on his cell phone. Trust me, I wasn't putting that call over the radio.

He responds within a few minutes.

Sam rolls up in his squad car and parks only a few feet from my new friend.

I said, "Sam, he's right at your feet; you might want to back up!"

Unaffected by my advice he opened the door, getting out of his patrol car. Now glancing directly down at this snake with very little concern or reaction, almost with a John Wayne-type gaze.

I knew right away that I'd called the right guy.

He said, "Is this the little guy Chief?"

"Yes, that's him, Sam, be careful, Brother."

"Chief, he's just a baby; besides, they can only jump the length of their body. But if they bite, they don't know how much venom to dispense, so we need to be careful in that respect."

Sam lights up a cigarette as he stands only a couple feet from the snake.

I said, "Sam, a smoke break now? Your next puff may be your last!"

"No, I'm good, Chief; I always deal with these guys here. It's common", he says, as he walks around his car to the trunk to retrieve a thin special metal pole. He uses it routinely to wrangle snakes.

He takes hold of this long metal tool, which has a handle on the end of it and reaches down towards the snake. The animal curls itself around the pole ever so naturally. Sam then carefully uses the tool to toss him up the nearby hill.

"Like that!" the snake slithers away.

"Puff, Like it was nothing."

He then glances to this right, and I see something catches his eye. He catches notice of the three hotdogs I used earlier, lying on the ground.

He asks me, "What are these hotdogs doing here, Chief?"

"Well, ahh, I, well, you see…. I"

"No, you didn't? Chief, did you try and lure the snake with these hot dogs?"

"Sam, not a word to anyone about this, and I mean nobody, you hear me, that's a direct order."

It took Sam about five minutes to gather his composure because he was laughing so hard. He almost choked on the cigarette he'd lit earlier.

"Okay, Chief, not a problem, scouts honor. I won't say a word."

"Well, if you promise not to say anything, I will give you a promotion."

"Really, a promotion to Lieutenant?"

"No, to Animal Control Officer!"

"Well, that sounds pretty cool."

"Sam, anyone who can do what you just did so casually deserves to be our very first Animal Control Officer, congratulations!"

"Why thank you, sir, it would be an honor."

Wouldn't you know it, it was a perfect job for him and a perfect fit for the department. We didn't have an animal control officer, and we needed one. I sent Sam to animal control officer school, and he was officially commissioned.

It only took about a week, and word about the snake story and my desperate hot dog attempts spread like wildfire. The Officers made tee shirts with a cartoon snake being lured by a uniformed Chief of Police holding a gun and hot dog. They sold like hotcakes.

I was secretly smiling on the inside; the incident brought a good laugh to the department and raised morale even higher.

***

We eventually made it to Friday night dinner that day without the snake, and thankfully they didn't wear the tee shirts. The next day was followed by Saturday golf with the guys and date night with the wives and girlfriends. I have to admit, it was probably the best time in my career up to that point.

The Vegas nights, the perfect weather, the pristine golf courses, my beautiful wife at my side, and not to mention my Corvette. Oh yeah, can't forget the car; I loved that car.

It was a great weekend, and that Monday didn't come up short. We were right back to the wild west, as we would often call it.

As I was driving to work the next week, I came through our Nevada security checkpoint. As I drove south down the road towards the entrance to the Police station, I noticed two individuals walking down the roadside along the "soft shoulder."

I slowed down to get a good look at them. One male and the other had very short hair but female features. When I slowed down to get a better look at them, the male, who looked slightly older than the female, pulled his hoody over his head and tried to cover his face.

Now, where I'm from, we call that a clue.

I kept going and called dispatch on my cell phone and ordered a marked unit to investigate the pair.

Something didn't seem right; rarely, if ever, do we encounter anyone in the desert walking without a vehicle and with no bags or luggage.

Besides, the girl didn't look happy at all. It was enough to raise my suspicion to have an officer meet with them.

Lo and behold, about 20 minutes after I got to the station, I received a call on my cell phone. It was my officer who met the two individuals.

There had been a BOLO out for the male individual, and he apparently had kidnapped the girl, who was a juvenile. He was in his 20's, and she was a teen. He had her get a haircut to look like a boy to change her appearance.

Her parents were worried sick and assumed she was dead.

It is hard to explain, but the Hoover Dam attracts so many, the good and the bad. Thank God we have a department in place.

***

The work at the department never slowed down. October 2010 rolled around quickly, and it was time to open the Hoover Dam bypass bridge.

Workers had labored for years building the new span, just as they'd done to build the Dam itself. We were told to expect over 10,000 visitors for the grand opening. My supervisor told me I was in charge of security and was to be the incident commander.

Not a problem; a thousand or 10,000 didn't matter, and a few extra visitors what the heck. I had this.

After all, I had already hosted two Governor's, cabinet-level officials, various dignitaries from around the world, ambassadors, four-star Generals, movie stars, and celebrities of all types. As I said, the Dam attracts so many people from every spectrum.

Over the years, we'd organized security for biker rallies, charitable events, anniversary celebrations, official ceremonies, and movie shoots. You name it, we've done it and done it safely.

On October 19th, 2010, at a cost of $240 million, and after five years of construction, the Hoover Dam Bypass bridge opened for traffic.

Officially the bridge was named for Mike O'Callaghan, the former Governor of Nevada from 1971 to 1979, and for Pat Tillman, an American football player who left his football career with the

Arizona Cardinals to enlist in the United States Army and was later killed while in Afghanistan in 2004 sadly by friendly fire.

The Arizona and Nevada Department of Transportation authority's jointly care for the bridge.

The celebration went off without a hitch, and we enjoyed a wonderful ceremony; no injuries or a single police call was made.

However, no sooner did the bridge open did I anticipated it would come with a whole new set of concerns. In law enforcement, unfortunately, you can never look too long at the good in things. Because something will always arise with a twist that you never expected. But you already know ahead of time that there will be a twist to every circumstance and situation. It's the science of law enforcement. Where you might see a nice new bridge, I see a new location where suicides will occur.

Another concern was the potential danger associated with high winds, which are frequent there. They could contribute to accidental falls from the new pedestrian bridge that runs along the span.

Even more concerning, the bridge sits almost a thousand feet above the Colorado River. It's great for cars to cross easily from state to state, but it arrives with a slew of other safety concerns.

Knowing this, I took a team of officers, and we traveled to San Francisco. We met with the safety and security professionals that managed the Golden Gate Bridge.

We toured the bridge and gathered ideas from a program. Why not, they had long since dealt with their share of similar issues. Made sense.

We brought the best practices back to the Dam and stood up as many safety and security ideas as we could. But it wasn't long before we had our first jumper. Then another, and another.

It's a sad fact of life, and we didn't have the resources to post officers at the bridge 24 hours a day, seven days a week. But we did the best we could.

***

As we moved into 2011, we celebrated the new year in traditional Vegas style with fireworks over the Strip and barbeques abound.

I had taken a department that was ill equipped, with old uniforms and morale in the gutter. I turned it around to become a department fully equipped and trained to handle just about anything. A new modern police department fully poised to deal with the concerns of the new era.

So much so that in February of 2011, my officers and I were featured on the cover of Police Chief Magazine.

This was an international publication of the International Association of Chiefs of Police. In other words, this was the "Time" Magazine for law enforcement.

We had made it; we arrived and built something great for America. Now, tourists and staff were much safer when visiting the Hoover Dam. Whether they knew it or not. We had the watch.

When the magazine cover broke, we all went out and celebrated; it was our 15 minutes of fame and a time to enjoy the work we put in.

However, a change had occurred with me, I had come and built it, but I needed more; I needed a new challenge now. I felt a strong calling and overwhelming desire to continue my work but on a greater scale. A desire to make America even safer.

I had been on this quest since 9/11. I felt a need to take it even higher.

It was time. Time to move on, to leave the department and turn it over to a new Chief. I needed to move on to protect the rest of America. I didn't want to see another 9/11.

I began applying to positions that interested me since leaving HUD Inspector General after 9/11.

The government created The Department of Homeland Security. It was years since I had first started in government, and I wanted in on this relatively new agency.

I applied for a position in Dallas, Texas, that came with a higher grade than my current Chief of Police job and just the type of challenge I was looking for.

My old agency, the Federal Protective Service, had now realigned under the Department of Homeland Security. Originally under GSA, the General Services Administration, they were now a better backed and better funded agency. Now, they have much more latitude to do the job better than when they were under the GSA.

GSA was a real estate organization; a police department didn't fit right under their business model. Homeland Security worked perfectly for their business model.

It was just what I was looking for, a much broader sphere of influence to protect more facilities and ensure our assets were safe.

The job was Chief of the Threat Management Branch for the Southwest Region for the Department of Homeland Security, Federal Protective Service. It covered the five southwest states of Texas, Oklahoma, Louisiana, Arkansas, and New Mexico.

The role oversaw investigations and managed threats lodged against federal facilities and persons. It came with a much higher pay grade and a 40% increase in my retirement. Now we're talking.

I put in for the job.

It took about three weeks, and I received a call for an interview. As a Chief of Police, I was at the top of my game and crushed the interview. Turns out that the Director was an old friend from when I first served with the Federal Protective Service. Who would have ever known he was still around after many years.

He called, and after about 30 minutes on the call, I had the job.

I broke the news to Amy. She was thrilled this time but said it would not be easy for me to pick up operations and move again.

Chapter 21

Welcome to the Department of Homeland Security

We are very well established in Las Vegas, and Anthony (our oldest son) was nine years old.

It was something I hadn't counted on; my kids were getting older.

I wanted to codify my family's financial future, and my career was the way I knew how. I was a public servant, committed, and in it for the rest of the haul.

But Anthony was not happy at all. I agreed I would speak to him by phone daily, and we would visit each other regularly. I would come home, and he could come to Texas until Mom got her transfer. He reluctantly agreed.

But at nine, did he really know that he was agreeing too?

There was just too much at stake. My family's fiscal future, everything I did was for God, country, and family. My wife and I agreed I had to take the offer.

No sooner did I accept the position than I broke the news to my department. Needless to say, it didn't go over well.

When I told everyone, you could see the essence drawn from their faces. I can't blame them; we were family; in the three and half years I had been their Chief, we had been through so much together.

Another thing I hadn't counted on was feelings.

I told them I loved them like a football coach would tell his team. It wasn't personal, I said; it was business, the business of a career. I encourage everyone to advance their career and strive for promotions.

Being promoted by the government was the only way to increase your pension and provide the best outcome for your family. Knowing this, they still took it hard.

We enjoyed a great going away lunch. Then the department presented me with a wonderful bronze eagle statue, accompanied by my credentials stamped "retired." This was so I could have them for when I eventually did retire.

It was a very nice parting gift from the department.

I traded my 2004 Lemans blue Corvette for a minivan to make things easier for Amy. You better believe that was hard. But she needed a good vehicle while I was away to take the kids to school and activities.

I drove the older SUV, our second car, to Texas. I rented a U-Haul and attached it to the back. The neighbors came out that night when it was time for me to leave. Everyone wanted to offer their well wishes. The neighbors reassured me that they would care for my family while I was away.

Amy and I moved beyond measure.

I closed the doors to the back of the trailer and said my goodbyes. The longer I prolonged it, the more difficult it became. This particular move felt harder than the previous ones.

I could see the toll it was taking on my family. Albeit, I had yet to determine whether this would be the last one.

Conceivably, there could be another promotion or another job where I felt my experience would be better suited. I was leaving my options open.

This moment was the most important. I hugged my children and then my wife. She whispered in my ear to be careful and that she loved me.

I leaned out and looked at her. I said, "Do you got this?"

She assuaged my concern by saying, "I most definitely have this; I've got the fort, now go, and don't worry. Call me from the road; you know the routine."

Just like the morning of 9/11. When she tells me she's "got it," I trust her. There are a few people I've met in my life that have "true grit"; my wife is one of them. She's amazing. None of this would have been possible without her support.

Hearing her say that was fuel in my tank as I set out across the desert toward Texas. Carting what I could fit into a small one-bedroom apartment, I rented sight unseen online.

Everything looked good; here it goes again.

***

As I began the drive, I started to check things off in my mind, conducting an inventory of sorts:

Did I forget something?

Did I leave Amy with enough food in the refrigerator?

Had I changed the oil in her car?

Did I forget to buy diapers for my youngest son?

Next, I did the same thing, only with the police department.

Was the department going to be, okay?

Had I said goodbye to everyone? Did I forget someone?

Were my officers going to make it without my support— emotionally and career-wise?

I think they call this phase – panic.

Yeah, yup, I am pretty sure it was panic.

I don't care what anyone says, lots of windshield time is akin to confession in church. You have time to think of things that would never have normally entered your mind on a busy workday.

A range of emotions begins to take place. A train ride through the countryside if you will.

It starts with a great set of songs, the windows rolled down, and you look to the left slightly from the slow lane), hoping the guy passing you didn't see you moving your lips to the Rolling Stones.

Then a couple of "old school" rock ballads key up on your playlist, and you're crying like a baby in no time.

Click, you shut down the songs, wipe the tears away, and begin to contemplate everything you ever did wrong in your life. It's good in one sense because it cleans out the guck, but in another sense, it totally sucks. Cause where do you go from sucks?

Now it's just you and your feelings. You know, the ones we always try to avoid because we're always too damn busy in our lives to take a moment to self-reflect. Yip, those feelings.

And they run deep, trust me.

They run the gamut from happy to sad, then really "friggin" depressed, back up again like the hill at Thunder Mountain roller coaster ride at Disneyworld, then down one more time, and you finally arrive at the station.

Well, I had yet to make it to the station.

The sun started setting on Route 40 as I crossed the desert into New Mexico. That's when it hit me like a ton of bricks.

"What the hell am I doing?" I thought.

"I'm 47 years old and just left a perfectly good job. Sorta "like" the familiar saying, "Why am I jumping out of a perfectly good airplane?"

There's a police department back there who is most likely distraught, not to mention my family is alone in our home in a town that wasn't native to any of us; what the hell did I do?"

Switching jobs at this age isn't easy or the safest thing to do. As a matter of fact, it can be "downright concerning."

Concerning, I'd thought, really?

Like I've said before, in cop-speak, the word "concerning" is often used in place of being scared. We never want to admit to being scared; it screws up our plans.

Nah, I wasn't scared; I was just concerned.

Risk is what my career and life have been about. Often more than an acceptable amount of risk. If you're not up to taking risks, then this business isn't for you. Besides, I had come too far to turn around now, way too far.

I stopped at a desert rest area just a short distance over the New Mexico state line. I needed a moment to reflect and gather my thoughts. Stepping out of the car, I walked to the farthest end of the parking lot.

At the end of the pavement, there was an overlook. I climbed atop a large boulder and looked out at the vast desert. There was nothing for miles. Funny, though, the timing was perfect; just as the sun started going down, it made for a magnificent moment.

I took in the beautiful, picturesque scene in front of me, wondering how I had come so far.

How did I do all of this? I thought. I had been through so much. I had put my family through so much.

I became part of the landscape and fell into a meditative state. The sun was still setting, and the desert was so beautiful. I asked God for strength.

I closed my eyes and stared into the sunset.

It felt like I'd been there for an hour; in reality, it was no more than ten minutes.

Eventually, I broke from my meditative state, opening my eyes slowly, and I felt better. I shook it off and walked back to the car, climbed into the front seat, and locked the seat belt.

Click! I was back to the reality of my decision.

I felt a little like the "guy" in the movies, where they portray that one special moment when the star of the film gets lost in the desert and undergoes some form of transformation or illuminating spiritual evolution.

In the hit series" The Sopranos," in the episode where Tony Soprano takes Peyote in the desert, stands up facing into the setting sun, and screams, "I get it, I get it," and begins crying and washing away his fears and concerns.

Well, that must have been what it was (minus the Peyote, of course) because that brief rest-stop moment still sticks with me.

A transformation of sorts.

***

I continued my trip and arrived in the Dallas area a day later. The weather was humid and about ninety degrees.

Honestly, it felt like "an eighth-grade gym class." It was hot.

Vegas was a dry heat; you never seemed to sweat. Here you lost five pounds just getting out of the car and unlocking the front door.

My new neighbor walked by and could see the U-Haul.

"Welcome to hot ass Texas," he said.

He wasn't joking. But it was true.

I called Amy to let her know I had arrived safely. Then I walked over and verified the number on the door to the one-bedroom apartment I'd selected online.

So far, so good; the community was quiet and looked very well-kept.

I used the keys they provided at the front office. I walked in and took a look around.

"Wow, I lucked out; the apartment was really nice and very clean."

"Whew," as I took a deep breath of the thick Texas air, "alright, this isn't going to be so bad."

After a brief temperature adjustment, I headed back outside and began unloading the trailer. It was getting dark, but then, all of a sudden, the military side of me kicked in.

I knew I had to assemble my bed before nightfall and then "get chow," as they say in the military. If not, then I would be sleeping on the floor. Thankfully, military mode always seems to kick in just when I need it the most. Muscle memory, I guess.

I set up my bed, armchair, TV, kitchen table, and toiletries and immediately hung up all my clothing. Then, I set out to the local grocery store and bought some food. After coming home and making dinner, I crashed and fell asleep in my armchair.

The trip and setting up the house were enough for today. I needed some rest before starting work that Monday.

***

Monday couldn't have rolled around quicker. On my first today in the office, I was greeted by the Regional Director, the Deputy Regional Director, and later my staff. They were all great people and ready to assist me in getting acclimated.

Texas itself wasn't new to me; I had gone through US Air Force basic training and Security Police School at Lackland Air Force base in San Antonio back in 1991. My mother was even born in San Antonio, while her father served in the Army Air Corps at Randolf military base.

But I had never been to Dallas before, so I had to quickly get a lay of the land, politically and actually.

I was assigned a squad of Special Agents who handled threat cases against facilities, people, and any other crimes committed on or around federal facilities.

You'd think to yourself, "What could happen on federal property, a crime even?" you'd be surprised.

Generally, a very safe environment, but just like the local mall, the buildings saw their share of the general public. We would receive calls for theft of property, assaults, missing children, auto accidents, and the occasional trespasser.

A trespasser would be someone in an office space after being told to leave for abrasive behavior. Or sometimes, they would be lost, such as the elderly. You never know, which is why we have to respond and investigate.

But our bread and butter were threats against federal facilities and people. I would assign at least a half dozen cases to my agents on a weekly basis. Cases came in from all five states in the region.

Patrick was one of my best agents. He was assigned to my satellite office in Houston.

Truly a good solid investigator.

A couple of months later, I received some news from Patrick after settling in.

"Chief, I received a call from the local Houston Joint Terrorism Task Force (JTTF) over at the FBI, they'd like me to be part of the team."

"Alright, we don't currently have a representative there now, so it would be a huge benefit to the department if they had someone like you. Have the FBI Supervisory contact me, and I will start the process. But before you do, I need help on a case here in Dallas. So, I need you to fly in for a few days."

"You got it, Chief; I'll be there as soon as I can." I could always rely on Patrick, a former Marine; he never let me down.

"Sir, we received another call from the Social Security office in northern Texas; it's apparently the same person, and he is threatening to hurt the employee's there because his benefits were discontinued," said Susan, my administrative assistant.

"Thank you, Susan; we're shorthanded this week and next week, too, so I've called in Patrick from Houston, and he should be arriving in the morning; we'll both will head up there as soon as he lands."

Patrick arrived just before the call came in; he phoned to let me know he'd arrived. I told him to wait there and that I'd pick him up from Dallas Airport. We'd have to head straight up there. The office was about 40 miles north of Dallas.

I picked him up a burger and fries ahead of time and one of those really good deli pickles for the ride up; I knew he'd be hungry. The least I could do for my guy was to feed him before anything popped off. Capture and arrest usually take a while. On the ride up, he ate, and I filled him in on the case.

I told him this was the second threat by this individual in the past week, and we needed to get up there and find this guy. I called the local police department ahead of time and arranged to meet the Chief of detectives.

We briefed the Chief and two of his plainclothes investigators familiar with the individual in question. They already had a jacket on this guy. A jacket is police jargon for case files; he was no stranger to the police and well versed in making threats to anyone he didn't receive an answer he agreed with.

In our case, he was no longer entitled to social security benefits, so the local office terminated his checks.

This didn't sit well with him, and he threatened to harm the office employees. It's a chance none of us could take; we needed to speak with this guy right away.

We jumped into a combination of two marked police cars and two unmarked cars. We first had the unmarked cars roll up to the apartment complex where the suspect lived. We wanted to cruise by his apartment. Patrick went with the marked police units.

A detective and I located the suspect's car in the parking lot, so it was a fairly good guess he was home.

He only had one car registered in his name. We located it right away. In the back seat was a brown rifle case folded in half.

Now, that wasn't good. Obviously, if it's folded in half, that begs the question, where is the rifle?

I looked at the detective, and he looked back at me, and we both knew this case just got real.

We told the other units what we had, and the Chief Detective went to the apartment's main office to speak to the manager. He explained what was happening and that our subject was wanted for making terroristic threats to federal employees. She agreed to assist, so we asked if she would call the suspect to inquire if he was home. She agreed.

The rouse was to state that the office needed to access the electrical panel in his apartment due to an issue with the neighbor's power.

Good story great idea, but no answer.

Well, that usually means they know we're here.

The rest of the units proceeded to roll in, and we all made our way to the subject's apartment. He lived on the first floor of the building, just across from the manager's office. As I've said, police work is not exactly like the movies, but in this case, it was a little like the movies; we surrounded the place.

It was then that my work from the days of executing drug warrants and conducting enforcement patrols in the New York City housing developments kicked in. I remember in first-floor apartments; the bad guy would usually try to escape from the side window.

Why not? It's on ground level, with no serious risk of falling to his death.

Fortunately, the suspect's apartment had two side windows in this case.

Uniform officers went to the front door, standing on both sides, leaning over, and knocking. That rifle was on everyone's mind.

I was able to get a good glimpse in the window.

Our suspect was standing at the front door, pointing his rifle directly at the front door. Aimed in and ready, had anyone stepped in front of the door or attempted to go, it would have been bad.

I ran back around quietly until I could see the officers. I made a series of hand gestures like I was holding a rifle and mouthed, "Front door!"

Again, unlike in the movies, we didn't burst through the door screaming police get down on the ground with guns blazing. In this business, you pick and choose your battles and take the safest path for the community and the suspect. Whether he cares or not.

So, we decided to retreat and wait it out. We learned from the front office manager that the suspect worked a swing shift job at a local supermarket. So, we figured if he thought we'd left, he'd soon emerge and head to work.

The marked units left, while the unmarked units stayed. A couple more detectives returned in unmarked units, and we took up inconspicuous positions around the complex. Ensuring the residents' safety while we waited and watched.

As they say, he was a cool cat and remained home that night. He apparently called in sick to work. Not to be deterred, we took shifts waiting for him to come out.

But it took until early the next morning before we'd see him. He figured we'd all gone home and gave up. Not in this case.

We ensured he wasn't carrying the rifle and was a good distance from his apartment. Then, as he stepped off the sidewalk toward the parking lot, we swooped in and made the arrest.

He resisted and put up a struggle. He was 6-foot two-inches and 260-pounds, so it wasn't easy. It took all four of us, but we safely brought him in.

My father had a saying, "Son, do you know why doctors are so rich?"

"No, Dad, why?"

'Because they have a lot of patience."

That chestnut of wisdom carried a lot of weight with me. No doubt this guy had the means and most likely the intent to carry out his threats. But thanks to exercising a little extra patience, everyone went home safely that day, and nobody needed to see a doctor.

***

In-service training is part of any law enforcement officer's career. Firearms, defense tactics, active shooter, legal training, handcuffing, defensive driving, use of force, taser training, leadership development, you name it.

Sometimes training can be fun, a good break from the street, and sometimes it can't be a downright pain in the ass. Especially when you're working full speed, the job, and things are going well. No one likes breaking a good momentum streak.

That's when the training officer suddenly approaches you on the way to the restroom, tells you your training syllabus and class dates, …..and makes sure you're there one day early.

Then they walk away. "Bam," you're tagged; it happens like that.

Training always seemed to be somewhere other than your home duty station. So, travel was usually involved.

However, no one appreciates the value of training more than me. It's imperative that you are up to date with the changing laws and with the state-of-the-art training methods & techniques. Regular training keeps you current in your craft and prevents you from getting hurt, especially should you get involved in a use-of-force incident.

The Federal Law Enforcement Training Center or "FLETC" is located in Brunswick, Georgia, and is the central training facility for federal law enforcement officers for many agencies, including the Department of Homeland Security.

I had been told to report for two weeks of law enforcement refresher training. Basically, it's a mini police academy with some advanced training mixed in. The idea was to retrain the basics of police tactics and also learn some new techniques that have changed over the years since graduating from the academy. Makes sense.

The Center of Excellence, as FLETC is so often called, was situated near Saint Simons and Jekyll Islands in southern Georgia, so it was always great to get some beach time in when you weren't in class.

Whenever I had training that involved physical techniques, I was always guarded primarily because of my previous injury in California. Losing my ability to walk again was not something I wanted to experience a second time. Not ever.

Class started great, and I was enjoying the legal refresher and the advanced active shooter response training. By the end of the first week, we were attending advanced forensic evidence collection class and firearms training—all great stuff.

The second week was "use of force" classroom training, followed by three days of very physical defense tactics training on the docket.

I stretched well every day, but by midweek of the second week, I started to feel a shooting pain run down my left leg.

We entered the "matt" room where we had performed "Red Man" training. Red Man drills are when you are paired up against an aggressor, the Red Man and you must use the training you've just learned to defend yourself. The goal is to try and defeat and arrest the Red Man.

This drill was intense, using a special training baton and handcuffs. The instructor was dressed in a red padded suit, head to toe, hence the term "Red Man."

Essentially you can strike him as often as you need to until they submit. Still, with their entire body covered in thick red pads, they usually never go down. Most Agents run out of stream during this drill before ever effecting an arrest.

I applied numerous strikes and issued dozens of commands for the role-playing aggressor to submit. I finally had him on one knee as I circled in for the arrest. I was feeling pretty good until….

The instructor blew the whistle. Of course, right before I finally won this training scenario.

Then the instructor shouted, "Okay, get ready for the next drill, multiple aggressors against you; everybody on this side of the room grab a training baton; everyone else grab aggressor pads and shirts."

Well, you guessed it, I was on the side of the room where I had to defend myself against three aggressors.

My back to the wall, and before I knew it, three people surrounded me, simulating a street attack. Each one took turns lunging in and hitting me with handheld training pads as if they were ganging up on me in the street. I understood the scenario, but it was brutally tough, even for role-playing.

As I turned to address an attacker to my right, applying multiple strikes, the instructor told the student to my far left to strike me hard. Well, he did, only I wasn't looking, and he hit me with the training pad on the side of my head and shoulder. I was hit so hard that my contact lenses popped out of my head.

The strike caused me to react immediately with a counterstrike. But when I did, I twisted my body, holding the baton in such a manner that I could feel something in my lower back give out.

I couldn't see at that point, but I never gave up. But my legs gave out, and I fell to the ground. I was still mindlessly swinging at the role players.

There was no way I could get up. As sweat poured down my face, I was in serious pain but still swinging. The instructor raced up to our group and blew the whistle to stop.

"You okay, Losito" You alright?"

"No sir, I can't feel anything from my hips on down; I think I herniated the disk in my back."

"Alright, hang tight. We'll get you some help."

"I shouted to the instructor as he was racing out of the room; crutches, not a wheelchair or stretcher!"

Just like in California, I wasn't about to be carried off the field. Especially in front of all my colleagues.

Dam, I was so "pissed" it happened again.

The doctors said this time it wasn't as bad as the first time because the disk didn't have any more fluid in it. I would need bed rest to reset the disk, followed by physical therapy again. I was so close to finishing the training and so close to retirement that I was fiercely determined to get beyond this injury even faster than the first time.

My sister-in-law lived just north in Charleston, South Carolina. I wasn't able to travel on my own; that meant no driving myself or flying.

So, she and her husband came and picked me up in their van. I convalesced in her mother-in-law's suite over the garage for the next month. My sister and brother-in-law treated me like gold and helped me recover faster than I could've ever imagined. I was bedridden for about three weeks.

Towards the end of the three weeks, I got mad, mad dog mean; I'd had enough of lying in bed. So, with every bit of determination, I shouted out loud, "This will not be fate!"

Again, I recounted everything I had been through and drew upon it internally.

I sat up, turned, reached over by the wall, and grabbed my crutches. Then I hoisted myself up and out of bed. I was standing on my own.

I slowly made my way to the door and down the large flight of outdoor steps. My sister-in-law panicked when she saw me through the kitchen window and sent my nephew Clarke Andrew to help me. Clarke was a great nephew and always there when you needed him. He knew I was a tough guy, so he didn't challenge me; he just asked what he could do to assist me.

"Clarke, how long does it take you to get around one block here?" I said.

"Well, for me, about 15 minutes, Uncle Tony, but I don't have a broken back."

"Okay, buddy, start your watch now, and time how long it takes me the first time."

"What! Are you sure, Uncle Tony?"

"Just do it, and stay with me, buddy, don't leave my side."

"Alright, ready, set go!"

I hobbled slowly, but like when Rocky got hurt in his movies. I was determined; I had the eye of the tiger, and the warrior mindset immediately kicked in.

Nothing was going to stop me.

It took me 45 minutes the first time. Then I did it again and cut it down to about 35 minutes.

That was enough for the day; I was physically and emotionally drained. But I was back. My wife flew in a couple of days later, and we drove back to Texas.

I took one more week to rest and attend physical therapy and was back to work. I moved a little more gingerly but was cleared by the doctor and went back to work.

I had herniated two disks in my back since I began my career. Let me tell you, it's one of the most painful injuries anyone can ever suffer from, but you mustn't let it become you. I firmly believe we grow through our tears.

I chose to overcome it and treat it as a life lesson, a painful one, but just another lesson, not the end of class.

***

Pigeons themselves are not inherently bad; yeah, they can be a nuisance and leave poop just about everywhere they go, especially on your new suit, car windshield, or mom's Sunday best.

But in this next case, the pigeons were unwittingly the victims.

I was back assigning cases to my agents almost a year after the northern Texas case and several months after my grueling recovery from FLETC. Similar cases as with the one in north Texas spanned throughout the greater southwest; there was plenty of work for everyone.

However, there was one particular case where my Dallas Agent, Steve Canton, would eventually come to me for help.

"Chief, I got a call about two weeks ago from security at the federal building in downtown Dallas, and they reported someone has been shooting at the upper floor windows of the building. No injuries, but they are afraid it could get worse."

One witness report stated the perpetrator appeared to be firing a rifle from an upper-floor apartment from the building across the street.

"What?" I said, "Shooting at the federal building, who in their right mind would do that?"

"Especially in this town. Do they not realize this is the worst town to fire a rifle from a balcony or a window? We lost a president here, and we all take anyone firing a rifle in this town very seriously", I said.

Steve had run down all his leads, but there were literally hundreds of apartments in the building across the street, and he was at a loss for what direction he should go with the case.

So, Steve and I jumped into an unmarked unit and headed down to the Dallas federal building. I met with our security team (our agency supervised the contract security officers in the federal building), who told us that they were concerned about the damage but more concerned because the proximity of the windows was so close to the judge's chambers.

This was obviously not a good situation.

We had no idea what weapon was being used at this point, so we walked up to the office space where the rounds were coming in.

When we arrived at the room, I saw bullet holes strewn across several glass panels. I'd say around ten windows were completely covered with bullet holes. They'd all have to be replaced—a big cost to the American taxpayer.

Thankfully the offices were empty and not occupied at the time.

I asked again the question, had anyone been injured since the discovery of these bullet holes?

One security officer stated, "Yes sir, the maintenance man, he was hit in the head while up on the roof one Saturday afternoon checking the air conditioning unit."

"Is he alive?" I said.

"Yes, sir, it was either a BB gun or a pellet gun; he went to the hospital, was treated, and is back at work."

A huge sigh of relief came over Steve and me, "thank goodness he is good."

"Okay, we'll speak with him, but for now, can you take us up to the roof and the area where he was shot?"

"Sure, right this way."

Steven, I, two security officers, and the maintenance man, Harold (who was contacted by radio to come up), arrived on the roof.

Harold showed all of us where he was standing. He explained how he was checking an air conditioning unit when he was suddenly struck in the temple by a small object.

I followed the path from where he was standing. I walked across the rooftop to the edge of the building. I could see the edge section of the federal building and the architectural ledge that ran across the building.

It was the section where the judges' administrative offices were located.

I also noticed pieces of the cement ledge were strafed as though they had been hit by what appeared to be gunfire. The building was older, so the cement on that particular ledge was susceptible to weather wear; it chipped easier than the rest of the building.

I could also see that the pigeons enjoyed resting on the long ledge. As I peered down the length of the ledge, I could see the bullet-riddled windows.

As I stepped back, I made the connection. I could narrow down, from the angles involved, a smaller cluster of high-rise apartments directly across the street, where the rounds had to be coming from.

I was able to pinpoint it down to about five or six floors, all with balconies. I asked them to head back to the rooms where the windows were.

I used a laser pen to shoot my path of the rounds and narrow it down even further to about three balconies around the 12th, 13th, and 14th floors.

That evening I contacted a firearms instructor from our office. He met Steve and I in the same room the next day. I had him examine the damage and potential bullet paths.

He came to the same assumption and narrowed it down to about the same few apartments, all with balconies on the corner of the building.

Now, we had something to work on.

Steve and I went across the street to meet with the apartment manager.

Lisa, the manager, was wonderful, and when we explained what was happening, she was shocked.

"Absolutely, Special Agent Losito. I would be willing to help you any way I can; my office is at your disposal."

The last thing she and the apartment building owner wanted was someone getting hurt and their building ending up on the newspaper's front page as a location from where people shot rifles off a balcony.

Needless to say, that would send fear and panic in the city. Honestly, we didn't want that either. Time was of the essence in this case.

We told her what apartments we'd thought the shooting might be coming from; she had names but wasn't too familiar, "I manage several other buildings Agent Losito, so I split my time between here and three other locations throughout the week, so I don't have a familiarity with all the tenants. Besides, we use a third party to process the applications."

I paused for a moment and remembered my days in New York City. If you need answers about any resident in an apartment building, the best person to ask is always the doorman.

Trust me; Doormen know everything. Next stop was Ted, the doorman.

We asked Ted if he was familiar with the tenants that lived on the 12th, 13th, and 14th floors on the north side of the building.

"Yes, Sir, on the 12th floor was an elderly couple, and on the 14th, floor was a single gentleman, but he was usually always away on business."

"Alright, Ted, so the burning question is, who lives in the corner apartment on the 13th floor?"

"I am glad you asked because these two young men were just told to stop throwing water balloons over the balcony onto innocent people on the street."

"What? They did what?" I said.

"Yeah, those two always look like they're up to no good. So, you're here about the water balloons, right?"

Steve pats him on the shoulder and says, "Yeah, Ted, we are here about the water balloons; thank you, Brother."

Of course, now we head to the 13th-floor northwest corner apartment.

I give the three traditional raps on the door. I could hear loud music playing and a blender going.

A tall, blonde-haired man around twenty-five answers the door, followed closely by a young female holding a blender full of what looked like freshly brewed margaritas.

"Homeland Security Special Agents, we'd like to talk with you."

"Not ah, for real?"

"Yo, fa real!" I said.

"Street Tony" just came outta me; I couldn't help it.

Hey John, come ova here, these two guys are from Homeland Security," John, the blonde hair man's roommate, peaked his head around the front door.

"Wow, so cool; come on in dudes."

In we go, "Thank you for taking a moment to speak with us; we appreciate you inviting us in; we just have a few questions."

As Steve and I stepped in, we immediately started scanning for any weapons and taking a quick head count of how many people were in the apartment. The last thing we want is to be outnumbered in an apartment with a suspected shooter and a blender full of margaritas.

Alcohol and weapons never go well together.

The three of them were apparently about to enjoy an evening of margaritas and Mexican food, most likely followed by dessert, a pigeon shooting contest off the balcony.

Steve began questioning them as I walked towards the panoramic windows. It was early evening by this time, and the sun had not yet set so I could see clearly out the window.

Bam, there it was the ledge and a straight view of all the broken windows right there in front of me.

At that point, it was coming together.

"Are all of you from Dallas?" Steve said.

"No sir, we all moved here from Iowa. We just graduated college and got jobs here in the big city."

"Really, it looks like you guys like to have fun."

"Yes, sir, we enjoy life for sure."

"Do you guys also enjoy throwing water balloons over the balcony for kicks?"

All three looked as though they had seen a ghost. "Well, you see, Officer, we didn't mean any harm, coming from Iowa; we have never lived in a high-rise apartment before; we admit it was stupid."

Steve had started with the easy question that we knew they were good for, in hopes it would get them to admit to more once they were "nailed" for throwing the water balloons.

Then, as I turned away from the window and gazed out towards the balcony, there it was.

A rifle was leaning up just to the side of the sliding glass door leading to the outside balcony.

I slowly started walking towards it while Steve kept them engaged in the water balloon questioning.

My goal was to reach the weapon before anyone in the apartment noticed.

I moved swiftly and stealthily so as not to alarm them.

Bam, I grabbed it.

In my head, I was saying, "Whew!"

"Oh, that's mine, sir," the tall blonde-haired man said.

"Really, what's your name?"

"Robert Sir, …. ahh Robert"

"Okay, Robert, what kind of rifle is this?

"It's a pellet rifle, sir; I brought it with me from Iowa; it's good for shooting squirrels at best."

"Really, how does it work on pigeons?"

"Ahh, ahh, well, ahh, sir, ahh, that wasn't my idea!"

"What wasn't your idea, Robert?"

"Shooting at the pigeons, my roommate thought it would be cool to pick off pigeons after we had a few beers, so we took turns, but he is not such a good shot; I am much better, said Robert."

Now we had them. Boy, did they make that easy? Every subject we encounter should be that easy.

"You can take it, sir; take it, please; we are very sorry; take it, please."

"Chill out, Robert. Do you realize that when you were shooting pigeons on the ledge across the street, you were hitting the windows of the federal building?"

"The price tag for your carnival of pigeon pouching is a staggering $10,000."

Their jaws dropped to the ground.

"Not to mention, you shot a federal employee, a maintenance man, in the side of the head, and you lucked out that it didn't catch him in the eye."

"We didn't mean it; take the rifle, please."

"The rifle is not the problem, Robert; your behavior is."

330

"Robert, I realize in your mind you thought you were just having fun like back home in Iowa, but this isn't Iowa; it's Dallas."

"This is the town where President Kennedy was shot and killed; you do know who he was, don't you?"

With his head down, he sighed, "Yes, sir, it was stupid; we weren't thinking."

Steve and I called the US Attorney and got the green light to seize the rifle; we gathered all their information and told the crew that we would be back tomorrow after we met with the US Attorney to discuss our findings.

Thankfully, it didn't turn out worse. We stopped the damage to the federal building, prevented anyone else from getting hurt, and helped the general public from getting hit with any more water balloons.

Who knows what they might have thrown off the balcony next after they had another round of margaritas?

Both roommates called home for $5,000 each plus court fees and received probation.

After they were asked to vacate, I am sure they moved to a first-floor apartment.

Sadly, you would think people choosing to shoot rifles in downtown Dallas wasn't common, but it was becoming more prevalent. In June 2019, things got far more serious following the big pigeon case.

Again, at the Earle Cabell federal building, the same building where our two suspects were caught shooting windows, in the early morning hours of Monday, June 17, 2019, a gunman opened fire at the entrance of the federal building.

Using a very powerful rifle, the former military soldier, 22-year-old Brian Isaack Clyde, shot at employees and visitors entering the building. Security Officers returned fire killing the suspect instantly.

Fortunately, no one was hurt during the event; ironically, the only damage was to some windows in the front of the building. It would have been much worse had he not been stopped right away.

**

By now, my family had finally arrived. It was early 2013, over two years from when I left Nevada.

My wife finally got her transfer to the US Department of Labor regional office in Dallas. Things were coming together.

I supervised cases, worked cases, and ran special events over the next two years.

Then in September 2015, I "caught" a break and was promoted to Deputy Regional Director of the Southwest region. I had managed my branch well and was seen as a rising asset in the service. I was honored to accept the new post and excited about the idea of the added responsibility.

The Director that originally hired me decided to retire. The Deputy before me moved up to Director. It was a natural progression. So, it looked as if I just did my time; the Director's chair was forthcoming.

For now, I'd have a slew of new responsibilities. I was now in charge of several large-scale security guard contracts, the firearms program, several other branch chiefs, including my old unit, the training department, the budget, and the entire fleet of vehicles.

This role was a much larger program than I'd ever managed. I relished the challenge; it's what I wanted. It's why I came to Texas.

Over the next year, I took off running and excelled at every angle. Things were "humming," as they say.

Then in July 2016, events would shake the nation and change the course of my career again.

Chapter 22

A Nation on Fire

"Tony, I need you to go to Atlanta for an internal affairs case. A supervisor there has been accused of harassment, and I need you to work on the case", Danny said. Danny was my case supervisor for the department's internal affairs unit.

I had been working on internal affairs cases part-time for several years since joining the department.

Disinterested third parties were hand-picked from around the nation to serve as adjunct internal affairs investigators. We were the ones that were usually called in to investigate cases outside of our region as neutral third parties having no interest in a region outside of our own.

The job involved a lot of travel around the country, which wasn't bad; I enjoyed the many different cities. The work was just the right fit; I was often able to leave my managerial role for a while and hit the streets to do some real investigative work.

Those who know me will tell you I have a reputation for being extremely fair. That being said, I didn't always enjoy that cases were about our officers. However, it was always refreshing when the evidence revealed that they were not responsible or cleared of any wrongdoing.

Our officers were very patriotic and dedicated hard workers. Still, accusations can be made, or a mistake in procedures can sometimes happen, didn't sufficiently warrant a full internal affairs investigation.

However, there were serious cases when officers or department personnel were fully held accountable, as they should be. The fact remains if you did something wrong, you are just as accountable as those for which we serve.

It was the beginning of summer, July 2016, and I just arrived in the city with over 70 Peachtree Streets, Atlanta.

"Danny, I arrived safely and have lined up interviews as early as tomorrow, Sunday. I have four officers who work the weekend that will be coming to my hotel to participate in interviews."

"Great, Tony, I really appreciate you jumping on this so quickly; please call me with an update by Tuesday end of day."

"Will do, Brother, talk then."

I conducted interviews Sunday and straight through the July 4th holiday.

Unfortunately, when a harassment charge has been levied against one of our officers, such as a supervisor, it takes precedence and must be investigated immediately. So, working through the weekend and the holiday is common.

Tuesday rolled around, and I called Danny to let him know the status.

"I have interviewed all the witnesses, managers are tomorrow, and the officer in question is Thursday morning."

"Gotcha, great, thanks, Tony; anything revealing so far?"

"No, nothing major so far; quite frankly, it looks like this complaint may be without merit."

Some of these cases will often look huge when they first come in, but after a few interviews and some solid detective work, the air can run out of them pretty quickly.

Others, in fact, will be the real deal and very serious in nature.

This one had a few interesting twists but wasn't *"panning out"* to be the crime of the century. It appeared I would be heading home by week's end.

As I took the elevator up to my room at the end of the day, I caught a glimpse between floors on the small television in the elevator car.

Alton Sterling, a 37-year-old African American man, was shot and killed by Baton Rouge Police officers in the City of Baton Rouge, Louisiana.

This happened when officers responding to a call by the owner of a food mart notified police that a man was in front of his store selling CDs and was threatening another man with his gun.

During an attempt by police officers to subdue Sterling, officers shot him when they reported he was reaching for a gun in his pants pocket.

Protests immediately began, and tensions began increasing around the country. Baton Rouge was my area.

I finished the remaining interviews with managerial staff on Wednesday, July 6th. I returned to my hotel, ordered room service, and finished writing my interview statements.

I started getting ready for bed after finishing dinner and my reports. Moments after I laid down on the bed, I clicked on the television.

Breaking news reports were coming in about an incident in Minneapolis-Saint Paul. A fatal shooting just occurred during a traffic stop made by the St. Anthony Police Department. A 32-year-old African American man, Philando Castile, had been shot during the traffic stop and died soon after from his wounds.

The incident, live streamed on Facebook by his girlfriend, Diamond Reynolds, immediately gained international attention. Tensions were already high from the Alton Sterling incident the day before; now, the nation was afire.

The morning of Thursday, July 7th, quickly rolled around. It was time to interview the subject of my investigation. I tried to maintain focus on what I was there to do, but I couldn't help being acutely aware of what was occurring around the country.

His lawyer was present, and we went through the normal paperwork advisory procedure, then went on with the interview.

It took about two hours to go through all the evidence and questions, not out of the norm for this type of complaint.

By the time we'd finished, I wasn't able to tell him he was cleared. Still, there wasn't enough evidence to substantiate the original complaint of harassment. But he was a cop also, and I believe he'd gleaned the same thing by the time we finished.

The regional deputy director invited me for lunch at the CNN plaza. We ate and talked about the region. He mentioned that he'd have another fresh complaint on an unrelated matter coming next week. He just needed to submit the paperwork to our headquarters team, which would trickle down to me being assigned.

That meant I'd be returning soon after this trip. I took a deep breath and laughed, "It's just part of the job, I guess."

He said, "I am sorry, Tony, that you'll have to come back with such a short turnaround."

"No worries, I am scheduled to head to Florida on another case right afterward, so I will tie in both on the same trip."

After we returned from lunch, I was provided with an empty administrative office and desk where I could finish my case report. I worked the balance of the day and got the case completed and packaged.

Danny had flown in from New York to discuss the case findings over a steak dinner in downtown Atlanta.

I reviewed the findings, examined alternatives, and determined that the evidence wasn't there to support the original complaint of harassment.

A slice of key lime pie was all that separated the both of us from the next morning and returning back to our duty stations.

Or so we'd thought.

***

As I dug my fork past the thick whip cream atop my key lime pie, I could hear yelling and shouting outside the restaurant. I placed my fork down on the plate and said, "Danny, pardon me, I'm gonna go see what's happening; give me a minute." I walked over to the large pain glass window at the front of the restaurant. I looked out into the street.

Crowds were amassing everywhere. As I peered down to the right to follow a large group of protesters holding signs, I could see them chanting, "No Justice, No Peace."

I knew we would end up in the middle of a city ignited by tensions. As we say on the street, *"Things were going south really quick."*

I ran back to the table to tell Danny. He was just as shocked as I was, so we settled up the bill and got a move on. Cops were not at the top of the fan list for these protesters, and our suits didn't help either. The only problem was we were alone. Not a good thing when the city starts turning sideways.

As we walked out of the front of the restaurant, carefully and looking in every direction. I saw dumpsters on fire, and the crowds grew by the minute.

We needed to boogie out of there quickly. This was not our natural turf, and the city cops had no idea who we were; besides, they had their hands full anyway.

Our hotel was on the outskirts of town, so we had a way to go. As we headed toward our hotel, driving our unmarked unit, the streets were consumed with hundreds of people, shutting down most avenues and approaches.

Traffic was bumper to bumper. Atlanta police had a surprisingly good grip on the situation; it was good to see.

Other than a few dumpster fires, the protesters remained peaceful.

A normal 30-minute drive back to the hotel from downtown Atlanta took about two hours, but we'd made it back safely.

Although that wasn't the end of the evening.

My cell phone began to erupt. It was my regional office back in Dallas. "Tony, have you seen the news," my Director said.

"No, we were fighting our way back from large protests here in Atlanta; what's up?"

"We have an active shooter here in downtown Dallas; we need you to return as soon as possible."

"Absolutely, but I drove here, so I will head out first thing in the morning. Do you need anything else in the meantime?"

"No, not much you can do from there; we have two officers who joined with Dallas PD and are engaged with the shooter. So, we need to go manage that; call me tomorrow when you roll back to town."

"You got it!"

As soon as I hung up after speaking with my Director, I received a call from the Deputy Assistant United States Attorney for Dallas; he was my point of contact who worked in the Earle Cabell Federal Building and Courthouse in downtown Dallas. The same building, we investigated the two young men with the pellet gun.

Well, the prosecutor needed to get to the building to help employees that were scared to leave because of the active shooter. I told him they were in the best place they could be at that moment, 'sheltered in place.' However, he felt obligated to see if he could safely make it to them to comfort them, be with them, and explore an option to get them out safely.

I admired his courage and dedication to his people. I told him to stand by, and I would call my officers at the building and let them know you were coming.

I managed to get ahold of officers located at the facility. They were about a full block and a half away from where the event was happening. I let them know that the Deputy Assistant U.S. Attorney needed to slip in the side garage entrance, so he could get to a few of his employees still working in their offices.

They said they would meet him at the entrance and let him in while officers covered his vehicle. I called back the assistant and let him know. He made it safely and was able to gather his employees and get them out safely—a valiant effort on his part. Not too many bosses would do that for their employees.

The active shooter was causing hell in downtown Dallas. I mean, it wasn't good.

The shooter was identified as Micah Xavier Johnson. He had ambushed police officers in downtown Dallas earlier that evening and eventually killed five officers and wounded nine others. Two innocent bystanders were also injured.

The next call was to my wife and kids. Unfortunately, in emergency events like these, they are the last call. "Sorry, honey." Thankfully, my wife is tough as nails and knows the drill. I am confident she had the home fort locked down.

We spoke about the event in Dallas, and I told her what happened here in Atlanta. She assured me the house and the kids were good to go.

By 2:30 am that morning, the police had stopped Johnson. According to the news reports and a subsequent police investigation, Johnson, an Army Reserve Afghan War veteran, was angry over shootings of other African American men, most recently the death of Alton Sterling and the death of Philando Castile.

The shooting was reported to be the deadliest for U.S. law enforcement officers since the attacks of 9/11.

We lived outside of the city of Dallas, but with everything going on around the nation, no one had an idea of what would happen next.

Ironically, neither did I.

I headed out first thing in the morning and returned the same day later in the evening. It was good to reunite with my family.

But the reunion wouldn't last long.

***

Three days had passed since the death of Alton Sterling in Baton Rouge.

The ongoing protests were a concern to the government, specifically for federal facilities, the U.S. Courthouse, and government personnel in Baton Rouge due to the event that occurred there.

Our regional office in Dallas was directed to send both uniformed police officers and special agents to Baton Rouge to protect federal facilities and personnel.

I was selected to serve as the Informed Police Commander.

My job was to ensure that all federal facilities and personnel were protected. Following the events in Minnesota, and Dallas, tensions were at their peak around the nation. So, this was going to be a very sensitive mission.

Before I packed up and went to Baton Rouge, I sat my family down for a talk.

"This is hard for me to say, and it's not meant to scare any of you; please believe me, but this is one mission I am not getting a good feeling about."

I looked at my oldest and said, "Take care of mommy and baby should something happen to me. Remember, you're the oldest; everything rests with you. I have taught you how to keep the family safe, do what I taught you while I am gone."

I felt horrible but wanted to ensure I never lied or covered up my feelings to them. Anthony, my oldest, fourteen at the time, was getting used to it to the extent anyone of that age could.

My wife was in tears, and my little guy, Aidan, only nine years old, was pleading for me to stay home.

I kept myself together, strong with lessened emotions but swelling with love for them on the inside. If I didn't, I'd fall back on emotions, and that would never permit me to leave.

Honestly, this was one mission; I didn't think I was coming back; really.

Tensions were maxed out around the country, and now Baton Rouge was the next epicenter.

***

I threw my last big bag of equipment into the back of my black unmarked government SUV. I gave my family a last round of hugs, followed by one last selfie, and I was off.

Ahead of me was a long drive from Dallas to Baton Rouge. I had plenty of windshield time to contemplate my operation, talk to my supervisors, and game out how I would keep everyone safe.

When I finally arrived, I set up my command in the annex building just off the main U.S. Courthouse in Baton Rouge.

My supervisors and I took a head count to ensure everyone made it from their various duty stations around the country.

We immediately began organizing shifts. The timeline of how long we'd be there was left open, but we figured it would be around two weeks.

As days progressed, tension around the nation and in Baton Rouge, remained high.

Although things were running smoothly, there we no reported incidents yet.

We took every precaution based on intelligence reports, so no officer or agent was ever alone. I had them doubled up for safety.

When one group ate, another group-maintained overwatch, we'd always travel with MREs in the event something popped off or we could not gain relief at our post. The only problem was those meals were high in sodium, and you could only eat so many of them before you just needed something fresh.

They'd ended up eating a number of the MREs and were asking if they could go to a local steakhouse.

I figured they'd earned it, so I said yes. But I insisted on a visible overwatch team at the table, entrance, and parking lot. We did a bathroom clearing as well.

Cops were not a fan favorite then, so we needed to be careful.

Restaurant customers felt good with all the Cops around, but you could still slice the air with a buzz saw. People were nervous and unsure of what would happen next. Once the first crew was done, the second team-maintained overwatch; it was the safest way to eat. It worked out fine, and everyone got a fresh meal after working 12-hour shifts.

Morale went up.

Then on July 17th, about a week after we had arrived, I was attending an early morning local police operation meeting just outside the city of Baton Rouge. Shortly after the meeting started, the radio signals lit up and "toned out"; traffic was coming in from every direction over the air.

Tones in cop-speak are dispatch alert signals over the radio that let us know when something serious has occurred. "Traffic" in police speak means radio calls and radio talk (conversation) between dispatch and officers or officers and officers.

The radio signal was for an "Active Shooter" in Baton Rouge. Someone was targeting police officers.

We all bolted from the meeting table and went to our battle stations.

I jumped in my unit and raced toward my command post. I rolled code east on Route 10, over the Horace Wilkinson Bridge and the Mississippi River back to downtown Baton Rouge and the U.S. Courthouse.

As I listened to the radio traffic, it was complete chaos over the airwaves. Everyone was calling in their status and racing to help other officers. Within minutes we had the U.S. Courthouse surrounded with double the officers. Over the radio, I sent the remaining officers to other key facilities around town.

No one at that time knew exactly who or how many shooters we had, so we took every precaution.

I pulled up to the US Marshal's checkpoint outside the courthouse, flashed my identification, drove through the gate, parked, and leaped out of my unit towards the command post.

Once inside, I checked in with my detail commanders to gather a tactical assessment.

We had a "Big board" set up with all our locations and 'posts."

I began to sweep through my smaller teams and gather the status of all personnel.

Within about fifteen minutes, we had full accountability for everyone. We were good; no one was injured. Now we had to manage this event. Information had come in that the suspect was halfway across town.

Two of my agents requested to head out and gather intelligence. I told them to be extremely careful. I performed an equipment check with them, and they headed out.

It wasn't long before we had streaming intelligence and a better handle on what was happening. It appeared to be one shooter, and the local police and state police were engaging him.

The gunman had ambushed police officers as they were responding to a call of a man carrying an assault rifle at Hammond Aire Plaza in Baton Rouge. The shooter would turn out to be Gavin Eugene Long, born and raised in Kansas City, Missouri.

He ended up shooting a total of six police officers that day, three of which would succumb to their injuries after engaging the suspect, and an additional officer who later passed on May 5th, 2022.

It was a horrific day for the nation, the city, and for our brave law enforcement community. We lost four innocent souls, all good officers, heroes that served their community and their families.

Long was finally stopped by a member of a responding SWAT team.

We would later find out that Long was carrying a 5.56 45 caliber semi-automatic rifle and a 9mm pistol, with another semi-automatic rifle in his rental car.

It was a bad morning for everyone and our people. We offered our assistance to our fellow law enforcement officers and helped in every way we could.

We maintained the watch for a few weeks following the incident until things calmed down.

Chapter 23

Internal Affairs

We were able to scale it down to just the officers who lived in the Baton Rouge area and have them cover the balance of the detail.

With that, I headed back to my duty station in Dallas.

Tensions around the country began to simmer.

I went on to deal with a series of events, ranging from supporting our regional response to hurricanes to training and operational challenges over the next year and a half.

In the summer of 2018, Danny, my supervisor for the internal affairs bureau, asked if I would accept a full-time transfer to his unit. He desperately needed help as work in his shop mounted around the country.

Not seeing a promotion to Director any time soon, as Headquarters had assigned a new Director to our region, replacing the previous Director who retired, I took the offer.

In no time flat, I was off to Internal Affairs as a full-time lead investigator performing investigations, special audits, and looking into sensitive matters that needed looking into.

Soon after arriving, I was handed two high-priority cases, one back home in New York City and the other in Orlando, Florida.

So, it was back on the road.

Only this time, I got to take the family with me on the New York leg of the trip.

They were excited. My oldest, Anthony, was born in Manhattan, so he loved any chance to "head back home." We consider New York (because I was born and raised there, to be our original home.)

From the time he could walk, whenever we were in Manhattan, he had the urge to break loose and explore the streets. He loves the city.

My youngest also enjoys it but mostly likes whatever his big brother likes.

However, I soon learned my youngest son had a greater purpose once we finally arrived.

***

The "Million Mile Man" is a nickname my colleagues gave me over the years. I acquired it because most suspect that I have driven over a million miles since the inception of my career. I like traveling by car, it seems easier, and I get to see the country.

Honestly, I have never kept track, but it's pretty dam close to a million miles.

It was December 2021 when my wife and I loaded up the SUV and headed to New York. The boys chose to fly and left after us. They'd already had enough rest stops and roadside restaurants from previous trips.

We selected a hotel in lower Manhattan near the World Trade Center memorial. We wanted to visit the site, so it was easier. My wife and I had never been back since that dreadful day. It was far too emotional for us to deal with. Our former office was now a museum. Not easy to take in.

The deaths of so many, the pain, the sorrow, and the anger we still harbored against those who perpetrated this attack were far too great for us to endure.

Emotionally, it was hard to process that the staircase we'd used to walk up every morning to our office was now an exhibit in the museum. We were on our way to work the last time we saw it.

Now, the country was memorializing the 20th anniversary of 9/11. Like that, twenty years had passed in the blink of an eye.

We popped out of the Lincoln Tunnel, and we were back home magically, just like that.

As usual, I stopped the car in Tribecca, got out, and kissed the sidewalk. Yup, that is how much I love my city.

My wife thinks I'm nuts and usually won't kiss me for two days after I do it, but it's worth it. I feel so happy whenever I'm back. She told me she'd rather I kiss a building than the sidewalk.

We checked into the hotel and called the boys. Always worried parents, but we were proud of how they'd mastered the flight and cab ride from the airport. They had the process down pat.

As soon as the boys arrived, we immediately headed out to one of our local haunts in lower Manhattan.

A French restaurant in Tribecca where my wife and I used to go after work.

After being seated, we all took a huge deep breath, relieved to have made it safely. There was a sense of ease being back in our natural surroundings.

Following a fantastic dinner, we enjoyed a nice walk back to the hotel. We passed by the 9/11 memorial.

My youngest son said, "Dad, I see you are looking, and I know it's hard, but I will take you and hold your hand, deal?"

We came to a stop on the sidewalk. I turned and looked at him speechless, staring into his eyes, struck by what he'd just said. I was filled with warmth and love as I stared into his eyes. My wife looked over at me.

"Honey, you go; he is your Angel now; it's time, and he will guide you through this part of your life's journey. You go; I am not ready yet, so you go first."

I was overcome with the love emanating from my son and a sense of grief as I stood there on the memorial site. I sorrow for all the victims and their families. But I knew I had to return and face that horrific day finally.

"Okay, Papa, we will go tomorrow before I start work on Monday; you can take me; it would be an honor, son." Papa is my nickname for my son.

He smiled and firmly gripped my hand as we turned and continued our walk back to the hotel.

Now he had a mission and was beaming with pride to carry it out. My wife smiled, and Anthony grinned, proud of his little brother.

***

After finishing work the following day, my family met me at the entrance to 26 Federal Plaza, the federal building at the corner of Broadway and Duane Streets in lower Manhattan. (This is where I have my case investigation.)

We grouped together and walked down to the 9/11 memorial site. My wife and oldest son shopped at a few of their favorite stores nearby while Aidan walked toward the museum entrance.

In New York City, it usually doesn't matter what venue you're getting ready to attend; there's always a line.

Growing up in New York most of my life, we'd all build in substantial wait times for shows and with traffic. You always added a couple of hours extra to the simplest things; it was part of life in the big city.

There are more people in New York than in any other major city in the United States, over eight million, in fact. So, trust me when I say the city never fails to let you know you're not alone.

When Aidan and I arrived, there was a fairly long line, but it moved quickly. After getting ticketed and scanned through security, we began the self-guided tour. Right from the beginning, my son grabbed my hand.

We both were in wonder; the museum was beautiful—a solemn yet serene testament to the victims. Every step we took was filled with caution and curiosity. I didn't know what I'd see; strangely, I was still looking for the entrance to my 6 World Trade Center office.

We toured the entire museum, and my son never once let go of my hand.

Toward the end of the tour, I came to an unexpected stop. There I was, frozen in my tracks.

I suddenly found myself looking upward at a set of concrete stairs. Not emergency stairs for the building or stairs to get to the next level, but a set of stairs on display as a museum exhibit.

The tour was like a fine balance of remembrance coupled with grief. I was standing where my office used to be, and the stairs I once traveled to my office. Honestly, I was speechless.

"Dad, are you okay?"

"Yes, honey, hold on a minute, Daddy needs a minute," as I let go of his hand for the first time.

With my jaw dropped and stunned, I crept slowly and closer to the staircase like I was lurking at a crime scene. Which, in fact, in reality, I was.

My odd amazement began to attract the attention of museumgoers and one particular tour guide.

Grace, a beautiful woman in her late 70's and Angel in her own right, gently approached me. She could see I was stunned and close to tears.

"Are you okay, sir?

Would you like me to explain this exhibit?" she said.

"Huh," as I turned slightly over my shoulder to acknowledge her.

"Is everything alright, sir?"

I broke my gaze at the stairs and turned slowly to look at her, "Yes, yes, I am sorry, mam, ahh, I mean Grace," as I read her volunteer tour guide name tag.

"Thank you, Grace, for your generous service in this holy place; you are a true Angel."

"Oh, you are quite welcome, sir, and I see this must be your lovely son?"

"Yes, it is; he is taking me for the first time here in almost 20 years."

"20 years since when?"

"Since the day of the attacks. You see, this was the staircase I used to go to my office."

"Oh, my God! I am so sorry, sir, I didn't know."

"It's quite alright, Grace, it's quite alright, although I should be the one who is telling you about these stairs."

She placed her hand on my shoulder and was so gracious with her benevolence.

She said, "I know a little how you feel; I live only a few blocks from here and was looking out my window that faithful morning. I volunteer here because it's my duty; it's my neighborhood they attacked."

As a New Yorker, I can tell you that we all felt that way. It hit us hard, right in our hearts. It hurt and still makes us hurt deeply as New Yorkers.

I gave her a big hug.

I found someone I connected with and felt that God had sent her to greet my son and me to make our journey just that more special.

After emerging from the victim's room, we finished the tour with heartfelt tears. The victim's room is filled with pictures of all the victims. We stopped and reflected before leaving and said some prayers.

We made it; I was able to start the process of putting some closure on 9/11. Now, I want to take my wife, and when she's ready, I will hold her hand.

***

The rest of the week went by quickly; I had the case wrapped up before we knew it. This was a special audit of a sensitive program, and I had done a lot of background work before arriving. So, the footwork on the ground went quickly.

My report and findings were done before we left town: next stop, Florida. My family flew back to Texas, and I headed south.

Route 95 all the way to Daytona Beach, then you make a right. It's I 4 West the rest of the way to Orlando.

Orlando is home to Disney World. I always love it when I'm here, except on business. It adds a strange eerie tone to the great feeling I cherished as a kid. Without a doubt, Disney vacations are one of the best memories on earth.

Only this time, I wasn't here to see Mickey and his friends. I was here for something far more serious. I needed to find a witness—a wittiness to an incident related to another more serious case.

One involving an auto accident.

I stopped about 30 minutes outside of Orlando in Sandford, Florida. I planned to stay the night and move in the next morning.

I often stay outside the target area when I run a case, so I don't contaminate the environment.

The added benefit is I can usually tell when I head back to my hotel if I'm being followed. It takes a little extra time, travel-wise, but for me, it's worth it.

It was late afternoon, and I hadn't checked my email messages for several hours. I was busy driving. I parked in the hotel parking lot and checked my email before unloading the car.

Mostly junk mail and a few bills. But wedged in there at 1:00 pm was an email from an employer. I had been putting in for jobs in the private sector as I contemplated my next career move.

The email was from the Secure Community Network or "SCN."

***

Now try and envision yourself running in a large marathon, like the New York City or Boston marathon. You've been training for years, experiencing every up and down life can offer, and now the big day is finally upon you.

"Crack!" the sound of the starter pistol. Suddenly hundreds of runners launch from the starting line with you. You're off! You're determined to win and not give up, no matter what.

Mile one down, two miles, three miles, you're pushing as hard as you can, your stomach hurts, your legs and back are killing you, and you can feel the shin splits forming in your legs. But there is no way in hell you're giving up, no way. You've trained too long for this.

Then you take the final turn, breathing heavily, panting. You're in the top ten, about to finish. You have gone further than you ever could've imagined.

You've pushed yourself through sensational moments beyond your limits. When in a flash, you peer through the sweat dripping down your forehead.

A quick wipe of your eyes with the sweat towel tucked in your waistband.

There it is; you can see the big banner that says finish line. In big block letters, it's straight ahead of you. Your run is now staggering limp of a jog.

You give it that last bit of energy you have left in your legs and make the final dash to the finish; it's within your grasp. Then, just before you get ready to stick your chest out to "brake tape," you immediately stop dead in your tracks.

Everyone is looking at you. The world freezes.

"What the hell is he doing!" they shout, "keep going, keep going, you are right there!"

"Don't stop!"

But something catches your eye. You see a man standing off to the side several yards before the finish line. He's wearing a dark suit with a black fedora. He's smiling.

You slowly approach him; with a sense of curiosity, you move closer. He extends his hand out and says, "If you stop here, I will offer you six figures on top of your government pension to join us right now."

"No more traveling; you can stay in one place."

"Run your own security program with your staff and have a brand-new office with a view."

"How does that sound?" he says to you.

"I don't know, sir; I never envisioned leaving the government.

Who will have the watch?"

"Well, there are others who need you, your talents, and skills, and you can maintain the watch for them, what you say?"

With a deep pause and a look back in the distance and back again, I say, "I need to discuss it with my wife and family first. May I get back to you?"

Well, that offer did come only from an organization whose mission was hard to turn down, The Secure Community Network.

"SCN," or "SCAN," as it was known to many, is a non-profit organization with the mission of protecting Jewish Institutions and the Jewish people throughout North America.

Was it time?

Chapter 24

Time to retire, or is it?

The email was from a senior leader in the organization. He inquired when I might be available for an interview as Regional Security Director.

Over the past few months or so, when I first contemplated retiring from the government, I began applying to various positions in the private sector. I applied to both security and investigative positions. To my surprise, the job calls came quickly.

From the moment I showed interest, I received about six very serious offers within a month—all six-figure salaries. I was very surprised and very encouraged.

It's rather hard to explain, but regardless of how great fiscally the offers were, none of them felt right. They weren't what I wanted or needed to fulfill my heart's desire to truly help people.

I was looking for something that possessed that special purpose—the desire deep in my heart to help my country, then it arrived.

The Secure Community Network answered that call.

I didn't wait. I called SCN that afternoon and told them I would interview when they had a slot available.

It took about two days to finish my work in Orlando, and on the last day before heading out of town, I interviewed by phone from my hotel room.

The initial interview went on for about 90 minutes. The senior leader and I hit it off. I liked him, and he loved my resume. The agency worked hard to staff their ranks with the best and brightest.

After we spoke, he said, "I'll" be in touch." So, at that point, I wasn't sure if I had the job.

The next morning, I headed out and was on my way back to Texas. I spent the next two days on the road and returned safely.

By the time I got back, I'd received a call from SCN. They asked if I would participate in a second interview in person. I said yes. So, I was on to Denver, Colorado.

Denver is a beautiful city, a "mile high." I enjoyed the ride from Dallas to Denver. The interview went great, and I was offered the job after I got home a few days later.

It was perfect, exactly what I was looking for when it came to transitioning from the government.

***

I broke the news to Homeland Security and let them know I would take the offer. After 26 years of federal service, just like that, I was leaving. It seemed perfect until the last day of work arrived. Equipment turn-in.

That meant I had to turn in all my equipment, including my badge and gun.

Then it hit me. I wasn't my badge and gun, but I was a patriot.

I looked at my supervisor and held my badge and gun for the last time. We both stared at them, then he looked at me and said, "You can still change your mind?"

Honestly, I thought about it, but I wanted to try it on my own, to go into the community and get closer than I ever have before to meet their needs without any bureaucratic strings attached. I wanted to give it a try, in fact I needed to give it a try.

"Nah, I'm good to go, Brother. Take it before I change my mind."

"Okay, Tony, we now have the watch; thank you for your service to the nation."

We hugged and went for dinner to celebrate. No big fan fair, no Bagpipers (except me), cakes, no formal ceremony, none of that. They offered, and I declined it. I was never a big fan when it came to me. I just wanted to quietly transition.

But truthfully, it was because somewhere in the back of my mind, I knew it wasn't over.

I retired on Saturday, September 28th, 2019. The next day, on the 29th, I drove to Denver and checked into my new apartment.

I found a nice modern apartment complex in the Denver West area.

I'd taken an extra day when I went for my interview to apartment hunt and found just the right place.

Unfortunately, my family couldn't join me right away. The plan was for me to go first, get acclimated, and then they would join later.

It was quiet, and the air was crisp and clean.

The drive to the new office was only about twenty minutes. However, twenty minutes in the other direction was Red Rock Canyon, where all the outdoor concerts took place. I'd chosen the perfect location, right in the middle of everything.

I retired on a Saturday and went straight to work on a Monday. Honestly, if I'd taken a day off in-between, I might've changed my mind about everything. I'll admit I'm an alpha male when it comes to work.

I believe work is Karama, and Karma is yoga. I will always work, no matter what type of work it is. Without work, I would perish mentally and emotionally.

That Monday, the 30th, I started my new job, just in time for Rosh Hasana, the Jewish high holiday. I went straight to work providing security for the high holiday celebration in downtown Denver.

***

It went very well, and everyone was safe. After my event was over, I reported to the new office.

"Hi Tony, my name is Sara, and I am Susan; we work in the budget department, and we've made you some dinner. We heard you came without your family and wanted to make it a little easier for you for your first week here in Denver."

"Wow, that's really super nice of you; thank you so much."

The staff at the local Jewish Federation office, where I was assigned, are some of the most gracious people in the world. They were warm, inviting and did whatever they could to make me feel part of the community. I was completely welcomed in the workplace. It was a great feeling.

I spent the next four months building a customized security program for the federation and the surrounding community. I collaborated with schools, education centers, community centers, Hillel's, and synagogues to assist with administrative security support, grant application information, training, and conducting security assessments.

I helped institutions improve their security programs and create the safest environments possible for the institutions.

The work was rewarding. Before long, I began connecting with various other agencies to coordinate support for our programs.

In November 2019, the FBI arrested Richard Holzer for planning to attack the Temple Emanuel Synagogue in Pueblo, Colorado.

This was a shock to the City of Pueblo and to the nation. The institutions I worked with were very concerned. This was my area. So, I increased my communications with as many of them as I could to assist with adding extra measures of security out of an abundance of caution.

I immediately planned a statewide trip to meet with institutions around the state of Colorado.

The trip was set for just after the first of the year. The plan was to coordinate with each institution to help them individually improve existing programs, provide training, and educate them on how to apply for nonprofit security grants.

However, soon after the first of the year 2020, news reports began to roll in covering the rise of the COVID-19 virus. It was January 2020, and information about people becoming infected with the virus in the United States was all over the internet and TV.

As I continued to work with the community to safeguard institutions and build supportive, collaborative relationships, I couldn't help but keep one eye on what was happening.

The year before I retired, I planned a trip to Disney World with my family. The trip was set for March 2020.

My statewide tour took place from around the first week of February to the end of February, just in time to make it back, head off to Disney World, and keep my promise to the family.

By this time though, the virus was an increasing concern to the nation. It spread quickly, and people were dying just as quickly. I considered canceling our trip.

But my boys pleaded with me, "Dad, we have waited too long; we will be safe and wear masks, we promise."

It was a big decision, but I decided to move forward and set strict rules for keeping a safe distance from others and ensuring they always carried hand sanitizer and masks.

Well, we made it and had a great time, everything went really well, and no one caught the virus.

The park was less than half full, so they went through all the rides about three times each.

After returning from Disney, COVID was now at full speed, and the nation faced a pandemic. Our work with the communities went virtual. Video calls were now the new way of doing business.

My work was now accomplished with selected in-person meetings, security patrols of institutions, and video training and meetings. We didn't slow down a bit; in fact, we got busier.

Over the next few months, the nation got into the groove of this new way of doing business, working from home. It had its advantages, but I still needed to catch up on the in-person connection.

Then May 25th, 2020, ushered in a change in the nation that would have a proud effect on the world.

***

The death of George Perry Floyd Jr. in Minneapolis, Minnesota, resulting from his arrest for charges related to a counterfeit twenty-dollar bill, would alter the face of a nation.

His unfortunate and untimely death would result in heated protests and riots nationwide.

America was on fire.

Every news station carried the story; despite the COVID outbreak, cities voiced their feelings in ways we haven't seen in decades. Protests turn into riots, riots in mayhem.

I felt the cry of a nation; I could feel the pain everyone felt. I sympathized deeply with the Floyd family and said many prayers on their behalf.

It sparked something in me as well, something that I hadn't felt until the moment I turned in my badge and gun back in September. That spark was a call for peace.

When I spoke to my wife, I discovered her job could not honor a request for her to transfer to Denver.

That meant I had to make a choice. Do I remain in Denver without my family, or do I seek to return to Texas?

The answer was fairly easy.

My family needed me.

So, I began to search for positions that would take me back to Texas. But as I watched the news, a desire rose within me rose, I wanted to help my country.

I began to speak to former government colleagues. We talked about open positions within a variety of government agencies. I discovered one particular office within the Headquarters of Homeland Security that was hiring for a new role. This new position was directly related to helping communities stop violence.

The job was to educate the public on targeted violence and terrorism prevention. Now my attention had peaked.

Bringing training and knowledge on preventing violence before it begins answered the call for me.

I read the announcement, and it was perfect. Although, that meant returning to the federal government. However, it was the vehicle that contributed to healing our nation and a way to return to Texas. The job was in Dallas.

With this new position, I could continue the same type of work I was doing in Denver, but now on a larger scale.

I couldn't help hearing the echo of the priest during 9/11. "If you don't do it, who will?"

I had to keep going. I wasn't finished yet, I needed to break that tape; I needed to finish the race and maintain the watch until it was the right time to hand over the torch. I knew one thing; there was more work to do. I went online and put in for the job.

Chapter 25

"I have the Watch!"

"Greetings and congratulations, Mr. Losito; we'd like to offer you the position of Regional Targeted Violence and Terrorism Prevention Coordinator."

Boom, like that, I was back, like Rocky VI.

Just like that, I had the watch again. Now there was work to do.

The new position came with a big territory covering the entire southwest tier of the U.S.

I said my goodbyes to the Denver office and all the wonderful people I had the ultimate pleasure and honor of serving over the past year. Many were sad, including myself.

Honestly, I met some of the greatest people on earth through this position. The institutions were much safer than before I came, and the program was officially launched. I handed the keys to the new security director, who was off and running. The community was in good hands.

It was time to move on.

I resigned from SCN and moved back home to Texas.

The new role came with several weeks of in-service training, and soon after, I was set loose to build my program. I expanded on the work I was doing in Colorado. I knew quite a few people from when I was in the area before I retired—a good formula to get rolling.

My new unit, the Office of Targeted Violence and Terrorism Prevention, was situated within the Department of Homeland Security's Office of Strategy, Policy, and Plans.

The mission of this new office was to work with the whole of society to build local prevention networks, concentrating our vision by seeking a resilient America where communities are united to help end targeted violence and terrorism.

I began my program by offering training to the community and providing violence prevention education to the states of Texas, New Mexico, Missouri, and Louisiana. The training was called community awareness briefings.

I combined this with violence prevention grant education and joining programs around the states with those who didn't have violence prevention programs—serving as a conduit for best practices.

I also sat on boards and committees to provide subject matter expertise regarding violence prevention practices.

I concentrated my focus on K-12 schools and then turned to the university sector. I attended large state training seminars and conferences to provide violence prevention awareness training blocks.

I was also invited to be a guest speaker at numerous safety, security, and law enforcement events.

In March of 2022, I was asked to participate in a joint violence prevention event established to celebrate Global Youth Day. The day turned into a month of efforts nationwide focused on *"Loving the Forgotten."*

In collaboration with nonprofits, county, and city organizations, including the El Paso Detention Center, I joined this effort to support a "Hackathon" for youth housed in the El Paso County Texas Juvenile Detention Center.

A Hackathon is essentially a workshop where groups of people join together in teams to solve a problem or create innovative solutions to problems. In this case, the problem was violence.

The question to solve was, how do we prevent violence from occurring in the future?

How do the youth in the detention center break the cycle of violence when it's their time to be released?

What would you (the youth) do to prevent violence in their communities upon release?

The youth were to answer these questions and manifest their chosen ideas in poems, written projects, and artwork.

***

The contest and my experience at the detention center was a life-changing moment for me. I met some of the best people in the country working with youth in America.

I served as a mentor and guest speaker. I worked with the staff and partner organizations to run the Hackathon and select award winners. The youth involved in the project worked extremely hard and were emotionally committed to the project. Prizes consisted of technology gifts, ranging from laptop computers to flash drives to art software and headphones they could use in their Pods. Their Pods were essentially their rooms.

I connected on a whole different level with everyone involved in this project. The youth worked hard to develop ideas to bring back to the community to stop the violence. The teams created dozens of campaign posters. The contest brought out the best in all of them. It was truly heartfelt.

Following the awards ceremony, the center's youth had a special surprise for the city. In their shop class, which consisted of fabric and metal working, several members assembled a Lotus flower made of fabricated metal and green canvas leaves, in the month preceding the program.

The flower, the size of a children's merry-go-round ride, was to be presented to the City of El Paso as a gift honoring the victims of the 2019 Walmart shooting. The horrific shooting where a gunman opened fire at a local Walmart store, killing 23 people.

Honestly, I was at a loss for words. This was one of the most beautiful gifts anyone could've thought of. Especially, because they made it by hand.

The second surprise was that I was asked by the staff to be the keynote speaker for the dedication of this flower. Let's just say, I wasn't expecting to be asked, and I was moved beyond measure.

The dedication was to take place at the Healing Garden.

The Healing Garden memorial is located at Ascarate Park in El Paso, Texas, and was created to remember the victims. The memorial features plaques with the names of each of the 23 victims situated in a semi-circle, each with a beam of light rising high into the sky. There are small waterfalls at each end, and the Lotus flower was chosen as the symbol of the garden.

The flower was selected because it represents strength, resilience, and rebirth.

I was told I was considered to speak because of my experience on 9/11. The organizers said I would be the best person in the group to speak about strength and resilience.

As the families of the 23 victims sat in the audience in front of me, I gave a beautiful speech to honor their lives and encourage those in attendance and the city of El Paso to continue to move forward in strength and unity.

From start to finish, the whole event will go down as one of the most moving collaborations I have ever been involved with. My heart goes out to the victims' families and all those who were involved in the program. Great Job El Paso!

***

Everything was going great at that point. My program had just hit a peak, and I was back to work.

Then on January 15th of, 2022, just three miles from my home, a 44-year-old man, Malik Akram, took four hostages at gunpoint inside the Congregation Beth Israel synagogue in Colleyville, Texas. It made national news—unfortunately, more violence.

The ordeal lasted for several hours with tense negotiation. Law enforcement and a variety of support personnel did a fantastic job. Eventually, all the hostages were able to escape citing training they'd received from the Secure Community Network. The organization I had just come from.

The shooter was eventually stopped by law enforcement officers and succumbed to his injuries.

Sadly, this horrific event seemed to be the start of a chain of frightening shooting events that took place over the next six months around the country.

Following the Colleyville incident was Buffalo, New York, on May 14, 2022. This was when shoppers and staff of the Tops Friendly Supermarket were attacked by an 18-year shooter who opened fire on innocent shoppers, killing ten people and injuring at least three others. This sent shockwaves around the nation.

As if the previous two incidents weren't enough, on May 24, 2022, nineteen school children were killed by a gunman in Uvalde, Texas. This was by far one of the most horrific violent events since the school shooting at Sandy Hook elementary school in Connecticut. This flat-out rocked our nation.

Next followed the Tulsa, Oklahoma, hospital shooting on June 1, 2022. Michael Louis opened fire in the Natalie Building, a section of Saint Francis Hospital in Tulsa, Oklahoma, United States. He killed four innocent people, three hospital staff members and injured several others before committing suicide.

It didn't end there; on June 5, 2022, at a nightclub in Chattanooga, Tennessee, a gunman opened fire on people, leaving fourteen injured, two dead. Another two of the victims were hit by moving vehicles while trying to run away from the horrific scene.

What was happening in our nation? Why so much violence? Was it because of COVID, racial tensions? The economy and jobs lost as a result of COVID? Or was it a combination of all these things?

I don't believe there is any one answer. But I knew in my heart I needed to shift the work I had done the past two years from just education to security and education. I began thinking and searching.

According to the World Health Organization "WHO" the world is still faced with emerging diseases, including COVID Strains, Moneybox, Ebola, and E. coli, to name just a few.

Faced with this continued threat, I wanted to help in a way I had never done before. So, I chose to get back into the security game.

Only this time, I would do it by supporting our brave scientists at the forefront of the war against these diseases.

Their job is to develop vaccines and hopefully find a cure, so we don't have to deal with another COVID pandemic or any other pandemic for that matter again.

I began looking for positions in the government that reflected this very cause. I saw the connection with violence and the pandemic.

Then, as I was scrolling through the job announcements on USAJOBS, the government's job posting website, I found it.

There it was like it was calling for me.

***

President Abraham Lincoln founded the United States Department of Agriculture, or USDA, in 1862. The agency's primary responsibility is overseeing the United States' farming, ranching, and forestry industry.

The USDA was a far departure from any agency I'd worked for, a historic and noble mission, nonetheless. However, they were concentrating on fighting diseases without a cure, like COVID.

They also have a unique mission of protecting the nation's food supply and public health. They combat biological threats involving human, zoonotic, and foreign animal diseases. This is exactly what we are facing now around the world.

In 2015 the Department of Homeland Security, together with the USDA, broke ground on a new state-of-the-art facility designed to research diseases relating to emerging and zoonotic animal disease threats.

According to information provided by the World Health Organization, approximately 75 percent of new and emerging infectious diseases are zoonotic diseases that may be transmitted from animals to humans.

I couldn't think of a better place to provide support considering the crisis our nation was facing. Yes, the shootings were continuing but this role would help in ways that our nation needed.

This new 1.25-billion-dollar facility had been undergoing construction for over seven years, and they were searching for a new Director of Security.

The role would be to protect the facility and our heroes working there. The work ahead of our nation's scientists was critical to the nation and the world. COVID had already rocked the world; who knows what was next?

I put in for the job.

Once the announcement for the position closed, things went pretty fast, at least by government standards.

I was contacted to participate in an interview. I was excited, to say the least. The interview was to take place in Manhattan, Kansas, at the new facility.

I cleared my schedule and was able to participate. I drove north from Texas to America's Heartland.

The ride alone was more than I expected.

I was blessed to see parts of our country that consisted of wide-open farmland, beautiful parries, and cattle as far as the eye could see. An amazing area of the country that everyone should have the opportunity to appreciate.

I'd been asked to assemble a "Seminar" for my interview. I was a cop, not a scientist, so I had to ask what they specifically wanted.

The panel said they were looking for a presentation of my credentials along with my vision for protecting the institution in line with the strategic plan.

Well, I'd just spent nearly the past two and half years since COVID assembling and conducting a variety of PowerPoint presentations for violence prevention. So, I decided to use that experience to sell myself on the big screen.

I firmly believe that everything you do in this lifetime consists of a series of lessons that prepare you for the next opportunity or adventure. This was no different; I was well suited for what they were asking and a pro at giving presentations.

The twist was when I spoke with the administrative assistant. She explained to me I would present my seminar in front of a selection panel and the entire facility. I wasn't aware of how many employees they had, but the facility is more of a campus; it's extremely large.

I took a deep breath.

"Thank you, mamm; I will be sure to have everything ready."

"You're welcome, and we look forward to seeing you soon; good luck with your interview."

I knew this presentation was going to be the key, or "lynchpin," to getting this job. My ability to present and be confident, well-studied on the facts and mission of the agency yet reserved and concise was the balance.

The advantage to this style of interview, known by some as a "Tribal Interview" (because you interview with everyone in the agency community), is you have the unique opportunity to bring your resume to life. Through pictures and a slide presentation, you can effectively pitch who you are, where you come from, and what you can do. I see it as leverage.

I built my presentation and practiced over the next few days, timing myself until I had it down. My plan was to use the first 20 minutes to present and leave the balance of time for questions.

When I arrived, the facility director walked from the main campus to the visitors center to greet me. That spoke volumes for me. He could've sent an assistant or security, but instead, he came in person to greet me. I was pleasantly surprised. It showed me how much he and the agency cared about their people and the process.

I arrived at a large conference room filled with professionals. The conference table was graced, with every chair occupied, I'd say about twenty. At one end was a large screen, and to the left, a laptop, were all the employees who dialed in virtually—no pressure there, of course. I took my seat after going around the table for the initial greetings.

It's hard to explain, but something clicked with me as I sat down. I could hear it in my head, clear as day. *"I've got this; it's no different than any of the presentations I've given over the past two years. The material was all me. Yup, I've got this!"*

With that, I felt a sense of calm confidence come over me. I relaxed a bit more in the seat. Then I just took off. Over the next twenty minutes, I crushed it with my presentation.

Follow up questions came in two rounds from each panel member for a total of about 20 questions. Some even had additional follow-up questions. I nailed each question. Everything I had done in my career had prepared me for this moment.

I was well-studied and had dynamic answers to each question.

Never run from a question is my motto. Don't dodge it, dance around it, fake it, for sure never lie. Don't ever, period.

If you don't know the answer, then tell them you don't know it. If you need to become more familiar with a particular subject, tell them that as well. But don't make things up or lie; they'll know it. I always say, give yourself the gift of integrity. You'll love it, and it lasts a lifetime.

I could glean from the questions what they were looking for in their next Director, someone who appreciated being a collaborator.

The facility was searching for the best candidate but one that had a deep appreciation for working across all internal business lines. Not a problem; I was an expert at bringing folks together and working across programs to get projects completed. Teamwork was what they really wanted.

I hit the mark everywhere. Following the interview, I was given a tour of the facility and the security department.

Everything was brand new, like a new car smell new. I haven't had the opportunity to be in a federal facility that was that brand new. It had that "new car" smell!

***

I toured the town the next day and searched for a place to live had I been selected. This method saves a lot of time in the event you're picked for the job.

There obviously were other candidates to interview, so it took about two weeks before I heard from the human resources office.

"Congratulations, you have been selected as the next Director of Security for the National Bio Agro-Defense Facility," said the staffing specialist.

I was blown away, and my family was amazed. This new position was not just the culmination of everything I'd done in my career. It came with a grade promotion. I had started my career in the US Border Patrol as a General Schedule 5 or GS 5 grade rank, and now I was a GS 15. This was the highest grade one can achieve in the General Schedule service of government.

Two years after coming back, I was on to the next mission.

Although it meant hitting the road again, my wife was far used to the drill. I would go first to get established, and then the family would follow. That was the plan, like all the other times.

I packed the rental van full of as many things that would fit into a 1-bedroom apartment and set out north. I had done this so many times over the years I was a pro at knowing exactly what I'd need and how many items would fit in the van. It is an art, trust me.

I found the perfect apartment within a ten-minute drive of the facility.

The beautiful town of Manhattan is like something out of a Normal Rockwell painting—a charming slice of America.

My first day to report to work quickly arrived on July 17th, 2022. I was greeted again by my new boss and new staff, along with the cast of folks on the interview panel—all amazing and gracious professionals.

Now, you don't have to like chocolate to work where I was hired, but if you do, it makes everything that much better. My new boss absolutely loves chocolate, and it took only a short break every day to enjoy some chocolate. Having a chocolate break with my boss was one of my fondest memories after I first arrived.

NBAF, as it's called, is hands down one of the best work environments I have ever had the privilege to be assigned to in the United States government.

Surrounded by an ocean of intellect, the best and brightest from around the nation have come together to conduct research and create vaccines for diseases for which we currently have no cure. My job was to protect their world while they protected everyone else's.

The mission of the National Bio and Agro-Defense Facility (NBAF) is *"to protect the United States against transboundary, emerging, and zoonotic diseases that threaten our food supply, agricultural economy, and public health."*

I couldn't be any prouder than ever to be part of this great mission.

Over the following year, I would work to build the security department, and develop the best ways to protect the facility and its scientists. My job was to make it for full operation.

It was an amazing feeling to work collaboratively with science to ensure the facility was ready to do the work it was meant to do, protecting our nation's.

I chose to work here because our country was still dealing with COVID and other diseases worldwide. My creed and focus have always been to protect America and especially those who defend America.

At NBAF, every employee, contractor, superhero scientist, along with the supportive community of Manhattan, Kansas, work tirelessly to develop vaccines to protect our food supply and nation.

Following my successful work fully operationalizing the security program at NBAF, I moved to my next role, providing security in the energy sector. With our nation striving to produce clean, effective ways to produce energy, companies are creating new and inventive methods to power America.

However, threats against our nation's power generation facilities are unfortunately no less a target for hostile actors.

So, I chose to move to the next venture. This next role is the biggest yet, as this new job is set on a global scale. My next job is as a Global Director of Security, protecting our national and global interests.

Stay tuned, for this next challenge, I'll need "to pull out all the stops!"

Final Thoughts

This is the land of opportunity, and you can be anything you've ever wanted in your life, whether it's a scientist, medical doctor, actor, musician, caring for animals, teacher, clergy, software engineer, artist, business owner, law enforcement officer, anything you can imagine, but one thing is for sure, we need to feel safe in our environment to accomplish those dreams.

Without that feeling of safety as you go about your everyday life, our nation will not thrive. Eventually, if it gets too bad, it might even crumble. I pray we never see that day.

That's the absolute last thing that any of us want. That's why I have chosen to continue to hold the Watch. Never quit, never give up is my creed, since before 9/11, my goals have been fueled by love. Love of God, Love of Country, and love of family, but above all, love itself.

I love this country beyond words. I have protected some of our nation's greatest assets ranging from the homes of Presidents, Presidential Libraries, schools, religious institutions, the US Olympic games, our nation's first nuclear submarine base, our nation's first nuclear submarine, the islands of the Caribbean, the Hoover Dam, and literally hundreds of facilities and key critical infrastructure around the nation; most recently the brave scientific community of the United States Department of Agriculture and National Bio Agro-Defense Facility, a billion dollar campus; now it's on to the energy sector.

Pride is an understatement.

However, what I can tell you from my combined 30 years of service to America is that the most important of all assets are the people—the great people of the United States.

In the scheme of things, I am just a small part of what makes up this country, but glad to stand tall with all of you because together, we are stronger as a nation.

I will continue to do my part to hold the flame that safeguards this great country, keeping Watch over our great nation, here and abroad. Honoring what I call, a "Sacred Obligation."

However, I have no intention of quitting yet; I still have the Watch.

Thank you for the opportunity to serve you, the American people, I love you and God Bless America!

Bibliography/Sources/Acknowledgments:

New York City Police Department

The US Immigration and Naturalization Service (INS) (legacy agency)

The US Border Patrol

Facebook.com

CNN.com

Police Chief Magazine who graciously granted their permission to use the cover and the story of the February 2011 magazine featuring myself and members of my department.

The United States Department of Agriculture - https://www.usa.gov/federal-agencies/u-s-department-of-agriculture

The United States Department of Agriculture - https://www.usda.gov/our-agency/about-usda/history

The National Bio and Agro-Defense Facility - https://www.usda.gov/nbaf

The Secure Community Network, https://securecommunitynetworks.org

Center for Prevention Programs and Partnerships | Homeland Security. https://www.dhs.gov/CP3

The Department of Homeland Security

The Federal Bureau of Investigation, FBI

The New York State Department of Motor Vehicles, DMV

USAJOBS - https://www.usajobs.gov

Timothy McVeigh Story- https://archive.seattletimes.com/archive/?date=19950508&slug=2119828

Oklahoma City Bombing — FBI. https://www.fbi.gov/history/famous-cases/oklahoma-city-bombing

Mike O'Callaghan–Pat Tillman Memorial Bridge in Boulder City, NV (Google Maps). https://virtualglobetrotting.com/map/mike-ocallaghana-pat-tillman-memorial-bridge/view/google

NBCDFWnews.com – Dallas Marks five years since 5 officers killed in downtown ambush.

Newsweek.com -Dallas sniper fire kills five police officers.

Foxnews.com- Dallas sniper who gunned down 5 cops.

NY York Times- Five Dallas Officers were killed as payback, says Police Chief

Nbcnews.com - Alton Sterling Shooting by Baton Rouge Police Sparks Outrage, DOJ to Investigate

Tulsa Hospital Shooting - https://www.foxnews.com/us/tulsa-hospital-shooting-victims-identified

Brooks, K., & Brooks, K. (2016, July 8). A call out to all to end officer-involved killings. The Hutchinson News, n/a.

Twilight Language: Wicked Deaths in Dallas: 7/7/16. https://copycateffect.blogspot.com/2016/07/777.Dallas.html?showComment=1468042895181

The Chief Newspaper New York City: https://www.thechiefleader.com/job-center-exams-city-certifications/index.html

Willy Wonka & The Chocolate Factory (The Movie)

Usbynumbers.com

Hackathons- https://edison365.com/how-do-hackathons-work

World Health Organization - https://www.who.int/publications/m/item/monkeypox--covid-19---other-global-health-issues-virtual-press-conference---5-October-2022

El Paso Healing Garden - https://www.elpasotimes.com/story/news/local/el-paso/2021/08/03/el-paso-healing-garden-memorial-honors-lives-lost-aug-3-el-paso-walmart-shooting/5468284001

County of El Paso Healing Garden - https://epcf.org/HealElPaso

Congregation Beth Israel Synagogue, Colleyville Texas - https://www.facebook.com/CBIColleyvilleTX

Those Officers who have fallen in the Line of Duty

We pray for their souls, their families, and friends. May the violence in our society end so we may one day enjoy true peace. Thank you for your service. We have the Watch.

New York City Police Officer Gerard Cater, his family, friends and colleagues, God Bless.

The Officers in Baton Rouge: July 17th, 2016

Deputy Bradford Allen 'Brad' Garafola, East Baton Rouge Parish Sheriff's Office

Officer Matthew Lane Gerald, Baton Rouge Police Department

Corporal Montrell Lyle Jackson, Baton Rouge Police Department

Sergeant Nicholas Tullier, East Baton Rouge Parish Sheriff's Office.

The Officers in Dallas: July 7th, 2016

Officer Brent Thompson, Dallas Area Rapid Transit Police

Officer Michael Krol, Dallas Police Department

Senior Cpl. Lorne Ahrens, Dallas Police Department

Sgt. Michael Smith, Dallas Police Department

Officer Patricio "Patrick" Zamarripa, Dallas Police Department

Special Acknowledgements

We especially pray for the victims and the families of:

George Floyd, and the family, friends, and supporters of George Floyd, God Bless.

Alton Sterling, and the family, friends, and supporters of Alton Sterling, God Bless.

Philando Castile, and the family, friends, and supporters of Philando Castile, God Bless.

Notable References

Normal Rockwell

Fast Times at Ridgemont High, (the movie), and Sean Penn reference

Woody Allen, Take the Money and Run (movie reference)

The Avon Company, Avon, Inc., and the AVON catalogue

John Casablanca's, and John Casablanca's Centers for modeling and talent development

The City of Manhattan, Kansas

The State of Kansas

Gate of Heaven Cemetery, Hawthorne, New York

Nextel Phones, and the Nextel Phone Company

Pepsi Cola Company

Coca-Cola Company

US Marine Corps

Sean Penn, and the Fast times at Ridgemont High movie

Jackson Browne, American Musician

The late Rodney Dangerfield

Woody Allen, Take the Money and Run movie.

Tom Cruise, Top Gun, the movie

Sophia Loren, Italian Actress

Mommie Dearest, the movie

In the Heat of the Night, TV series

Deliverance, the movie

James Bond, and the James Bond movie series

Mission Impossible, the movie series

WWE & Stone-Cold Steve Austin

Embers Steakhouse, and Lou Rocanelli, Founder, Brooklyn, New York

Vinnies Meat market, Brooklyn, New York

Loni Anderson

Lifetime TV

James Taylor, Up on the Roof, the song

Last Action Hero, starring Arnold Schwarzenegger & Frank McRae

Wendys, "Where's the Beef" commercial.

Little Rascals Comedy Show

Liam Neeson, Michael Collins, the movie

Viva Las Vegas, Starring Elvis Presley

Vegas Vacation, the movie

The Transformers, the movie series

Shark Week, the Discovery Channel

The Sopranos, the series, HBO

ZZ top, the music band

Made in United States
North Haven, CT
12 August 2023

40231524R00240